Hey,
You Never Know

Hey,
You Never Know

*Three Jewish families
In the Twentieth Century:
Stories of Struggle and Love*

Robert Newman

Published by Visions Communications, New York, NY

Personal Acknowledgement

To my sons, their spouses and their children. In hope that your lives will be richer if you know more about the world I came from.

To Bette Alexander, without whose loving support these stories would never have been written.

Creative Acknowledgement

To Bette Alexander, a talented artist whose work is portrayed on the cover of this book. Please find more information at *www.bettealexander.com*

To Anthony Picco, whose knowledge of graphic arts and the creative world took on special meaning in the preparation and presentation of this book. He can be e-mailed at *aspicco@gmail.com*

Copyright @ 2009 by Robert Newman

Published by Visions Communications, New York, NY

Library of Congress Control Number: 2009939094
ISBN: 978-1-885750-07-5

This book was printed in the United States of America.

To order additional copies of this book, or schedule an author reading and signing, contact:
Beth Bay
Visions Communications
212-529-4029
bethbay@gmail.com
www.heyyouneverknowthebook.com

Contents

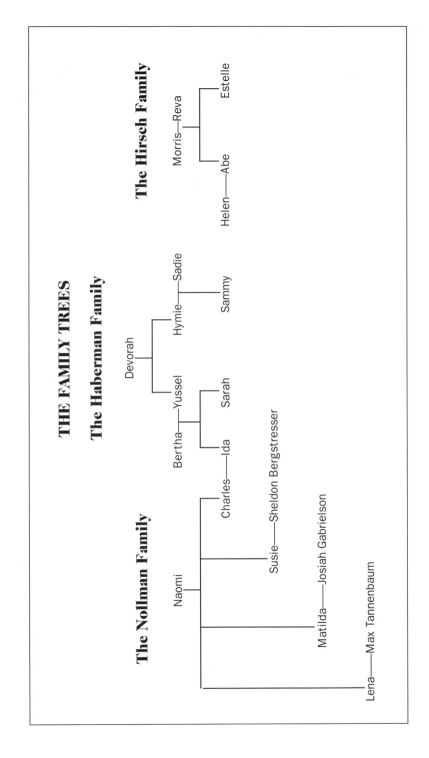

Part One:
The Haberman Family

1. How the Midwife Saved Bertha

A cramping pain awakened Bertha who put both hands on her big belly. The life inside her was stirring again. She herself had slept poorly for weeks. She turned her head to look at the bedroom window; the shade, pulled down to the sill, glowed in the early morning sunlight. She heard the clatter of a pan in the kitchen. Her mother-in-law was heating her morning water to be sipped through a sugar cube. Devorah believed in making noise when others were still asleep.

Bertha closed her eyes. She wanted another hour of daydreams about her baby, sometimes in her fantasies a boy, sometimes a girl. She did not want to have to share her happiness, her treasure, with her mother-in-law who would be watching and, whatever the circumstances, find much to criticize.

Bertha sighed deeply and closed her eyes until she winced because of another sharp pain. "Mein Gott." She poked her husband in the ribs. "Yussel, it is time. Send the boy."

For a moment, Yussel, a string bean of a man who for several months had been pushed to the edge of the bed by his tall, expanding wife, waggled his knees under the patchwork quilt to show reluctance, stared at the ceiling of the bedroom and said, "Oy, vey."

Yussel leapt from the bed, ran to the door of the flat and down the stairs, pulling his overcoat over his nightshirt. He paused and said, "Hurry, hurry." He yanked open the front door and was greeted by a *viese velt*, a white world; it had snowed overnight. Heavy dark clouds seemed to sit on the tops of the two-story houses. Yussel stepped back into his house and slid his bare feet into galoshes. He ran to the next house and pounded on the door. "Herschel," he shouted. "It is time. Send the boy. Send down Meir."

Lights turned on in Herschel's second-floor flat. There were high-pitched protests. After an impatient delay, the door opened. Meir, a small boy in knickers, long stockings, coat, hat, boots, mittens and a scarlet muffler, ran to the sidewalk where Yussel waited.

Herschel, in pajamas, waved from his doorway and shouted, "Oy, it snowed. Vey iz mere." He stared at Yussel. "I wish mazel to Bertha and to you." He paused. "Not that there is anything you can do." He spoke with some authority, having been through this experience.

Yussel held out both hands, palms up and called out, "What can I do? Nothing."

Herschel called out, "Do you know about Shifra? She was Moses's midwife."

"I know," Yussel said, "another Shifra."

Herschel laughed, "But our Shifra's name is yet her destiny."

They stared at each other. "Yes," Yussel said. "Perhaps I will be the father of another Moses." Hershel waved and shut the door.

Yussel grabbed Meir's arm and thrust a scrap of paper at him. "The lady's address, Meir. Her address. Twenty twenty-five Mack Avenue."

The boy looked up at him, bewildered.

"Meir!" Yussel shook his arm. "Wake up."

Meir blinked.

Yussel was stern. "It is Bertha's time. You must fetch the lady."

Meir smiled. His eyes closed.

"Five cents, Meir," Yussel reminded. Meir nodded.

"Where is the paper, Meir?"

Meir raised his arm and looked at the paper in his mittened hand.

Yussel patted his head. "Put the paper in your pocket. You must run."

The boy tensed, readying himself, staring in the direction he was going to go.

"Meir, my fine runner!" Yussel said. "Go, go."

Meir looked at him, blinking again, his jaw moving.

"Five cents more if the lady comes before your mother prepares breakfast."

Meir took three deep breaths and started off in a mad sprint. Yussel watched until the boy turned the corner. He looked up, his eye caught by a movement of the lace curtain in his living room. He glimpsed a hand on the curtain. He knew that his mother had witnessed Meir's departure. Yussel sighed. Devorah, an impatient soul, would be waiting for the plan to fail. What could happen? Meir could get lost; the lady, for some reason, would not come. And his mother would blame him. It was the story of his life in this country: no matter what happened or who caused it, Devorah believed that Yussel was at fault. He was responsible for bringing her to this city to live with him and his young wife, a girl whom his mother told Yussel behind Bertha's back knew nothing about kashruth, God's laws according to which all Jews must live.

No, Yussel thought, that was not his real fault. The accusation underlying all of his mother's complaints was that Yussel was not his father. Devorah first blamed Haim for dying, and then accused Yussel of not being Haim. *Guilty*, Yussel thought bitterly. *Guilty, Mother.* And to make matters worse, he had married Bertha and gotten her pregnant. "I broke no commandments," he reflected. "The Lord knows."

Standing in the snow in rubber galoshes, he became aware that his feet hurt. He hobbled to the front door, threw off his galoshes and limped up the stairs. He saw Devorah going to the bedroom with towels.

"Her water broke," his mother called out in Yiddish. "Where is the woman?" she asked, though she had to know that the midwife could not possibly be there yet.

Yussel followed her to the bedroom. Bertha murmured and twisted on the bed.

"Bertha?" he said.

Devorah, applying the towels, looked back at him. In an angry voice, she said, "Wait in the hall."

Frowning at his mother, Yussel nevertheless backed out of the room. His mission had been to send Meir for the midwife; he had no further role to play. He paced the hall outside of the bedroom and imagined Meir dashing down the snow-covered streets.

After running a block at top speed, Meir slowed to a steady lope. Fifteen minutes later, reeling and gulping deep breaths that rattled in and out of his narrow chest, he arrived at the house twenty blocks away. He banged on the front door. "Lady, lady. It's me, Meir. It is time. Mr. Haberman says it is time."

Upstairs, a woman raised a window and called down, "Stop shouting, little boy. I am coming. Shifra comes, little boy."

Meir stood shivering and thinking about little colored candy drops pasted to paper strips that he would buy unless his father forced him to save the ten cents.

The lady emerged from the house carrying a black leather satchel. She touched his arm. "Come. We will take the trolley."

Shifra liked the trolley. At her stop at Mack and Woodward, with Meir shivering beside her, she waited in the frozen early morning wearing her black shawl over a heavy wool sweater, her red babushka tied under her chin, her feet warm in woolen stockings and the fine leather boots she had carried from the old country. With the satchel in her hand, stomping and swinging her free arm, her breath pluming, Shifra reflected that the cold in America was no less bitter than the cold in Russia. But there in her shtetl, she had never seen, much less imagined, an electric trolley on rails. Now, only a year in the city of Detroit, Michigan, USA, she was a frequent rider on the rocking yellow cars that carried her to birthings up and down Woodward Avenue.

Shifra heard the clanging bell and saw the trolley down the line. She thought that the car moved slowly, but as it approached from its stop at Watson, it seemed to move faster. "Could it be?" she wondered.

The trolley halted. Shifra gripped the pole and, pushing Meir ahead of her, stepped into the car. She dropped six cents into the glass box. "Kirby Street," she said to the conductor who was half asleep. She recognized this man with his long, drooping mustache and his red hair curly under his cap. "Kirby Street," she repeated until their eyes met, and she was certain he had heard her. She knew she would doze in the warm car.

Two other passengers, men, possibly on their way home from the riverboats, were asleep. Shifra settled next to Meir on the polished wicker seat near the coal heater. Swaying with the trolley, her black satchel between her legs, tucked under her ankle-length skirt, she sighed and loosened her shawl. Shifra let her eyes close. The boy was already deep asleep.

After a time, she awoke, momentarily confused by the motorman's clanging of the trolley bell; a milk van and horse had stopped on the car tracks. Goaded by the insistent bell, the driver of the van shouted at his horse and snapped the reins until the animal slowly pulled the wagon off the tracks. The trolley moved forward and stopped. Shifra looked at the conductor who nodded yes; it was Kirby Street.

In the cold again, pulling Meir by the hand, the sharp wind hurting her nose and eyes, a block from her destination she saw two young men pacing in front of a house, the only others outside on this chilled morning. They saw her as she saw them, and she knew from the way they stood, slightly bent forward, hands on hips, that they were measuring her deliberate progress.

When I was a young girl, she thought, *I was a fast walker. Now, my legs are heavy, but I still get to where I'm going. So don't hurry me, young men.*

Yussel spoke as she arrived, "Du bist arroyz. You are here. Thank God." Meir ran to the other man who swept him up and moved toward his house.

"Thank you, thank you, Herschel," Yussel called to his neighbor who was kissing his son. "Thank you, Meir. I will reward you later."

Yussel led Shifra into his house. She grunted as she followed him up the steep stairs to the second-floor flat. "She's here at last, Gut se danken," he said to Devorah who stood stiffly in the living room, frowning, her arms folded.

"Mineh mutter," Yussel said.

A woman who awaits the worst, Shifra thought.

The flat was not well heated. Devorah wore a gray sweater, a blue shawl and black woolen stockings; her gray hair was pulled back and wound into a bun. "In here," she said, leading Shifra down a long hall to a small bedroom at the back of the flat.

The room was lit by one bulb hanging from the ceiling and by flickering candles of various lengths set on the dresser, on a nightstand next to the bed and on the sill of the window. Near Bertha's head waited a white wicker cradle on rockers. A cane-seated rocking chair was placed in the corner. On a small table sat a bowl of water with steam rising and clean white cloths that Shifra could see were torn from a sheet.

Shifra closed the door, shutting out Yussel who had been trying to catch sight of his wife on the bed. "Vous is dei nomen?" Shifra said to Bertha who was breathing deeply, her eyes bright with anxiety.

"Bertha," her mother-in-law said.

A woman who answers for others, Shifra thought.

Bertha, who was preoccupied with her body, glared at her mother-in-law who did not mind. Bertha groaned. Shifra nodded and pulled off the blanket. "Let us see." Bertha's abdomen protruded hugely. Shifra inserted two fingers into Bertha's vagina and estimated the size of the cervix. "The baby is not ready," she told them in Yiddish.

She looked at the towels Devorah had used when Bertha's water broke. "Gut," she said when they showed no sign of blood. She covered Bertha and asked for tea for herself and the expectant mother.

Devorah shrugged and went to the kitchen. "Not soon," she told Yussel.

Bertha wanted this birthing to be done with. She was confused about the process. Her water had broken, but where was the baby? She was dazed with anxiety and intermittent pain. She was in the hands of a stranger who seemed confident, but told her almost nothing. "Be patient, little mother. We are in the hands of the good Lord." Her enemy, Devorah, hovered, a crow expecting calamity. Bertha had never felt so helpless, so unable to control her body. She cried out, "Oy, oy, oy!"

Seated at the kitchen table, his head in his hands, Yussel responded, "Ai, ai, ai."

It was afternoon before the frequency of the pains stirred Shifra to action. She turned to Devorah. "Hold her shoulders. Help her sit up. I am going to turn her."

Shifra, smiling at Bertha, took a rubber sheet out of her bag, laid it across the bed, and pivoted Bertha so that she lay on the sheet, her legs apart, her knees raised. As the baby emerged, it would drop into Shifra's hands.

Her lips compressed into a thin line, Bertha laughed briefly at the spectacle of being turned on her bed like a great turtle. Shifra opened the clasp on her black bag and took out a small stopper bottle. "Schmaltz," she explained and coated Bertha's vagina up to her cervix with chicken fat. Shifra reached into her bag for tools of her trade, scissors and a piece of string, and placed them on the bed.

"Wipe her face, hold her hand," she commanded Devorah who frowned, but obeyed.

Bertha was strong. As the contractions came more frequently, she fixed her eyes on the top of Shifra's head and cried out only a few times.

A woman of the land, Shifra thought. "It's all right to cry out," she told Bertha. "But you must push when I tell you. And do not push when I say wait."

Within thirty minutes, a baby girl was born. She cried loudly; the three women smiled. Shifra used string to tie the cord and her scissors to cut it. She cleaned the infant with a soft, warm damp cloth and turned to hand the baby to the waiting mother. Devorah muttered a warning. A heavy flow of blood was draining onto the rubber sheet. Devorah muttered, "Oy vey. It is the demon Lilith."

Bertha blinked her eyes rapidly and looked up at Shifra. "Nischt Lilith?"

"Shah," Shifra said. "Nisht Lilith. Nisht schecht. It is nothing." She quickly placed the crying baby into the cradle. She told Devorah to help, and the two women lifted Bertha and carried her to the bathroom, ignoring Yussel who cried out, "Vus, vus?" first to Shifra then to his mother.

"Look to your baby," Shifra said to him.

Yussel ran to the bedroom and saw the baby in the cradle. She was sleeping. He hurried to the bathroom in time to watch Shifra place Bertha, who was pale but calm, into the bathtub. Shifra ran the cold water, which she tempered with a lesser flow from the hot water faucet. She let the cooling water rise to Bertha's hips. Yussel backed into a corner of the room, bobbing his head and praying. Within moments, the bleeding slowed to a trickle.

"Danken Got," Devorah said.

Shifra stroked Bertha's head and murmured encouragement. She signaled Yussel to help lift his wife out of the tub and carry her back to the bed. Nodding at the rubber sheet, she said to Devorah, who now seemed docile and uncertain, "Take it away."

Devorah carefully folded the rubber sheet, with its pool of blood, and took it to the bathroom.

She is unsettled by this good fortune, Shifra thought. She gently dried Bertha with a towel and covered her with the blanket. Devorah approached with another blanket. Shifra held up her hand. "Not too cool, not too warm. You can rub her feet with the towel." She handed the squalling infant to her smiling mother.

Yussel, hovering, wiped his tears.

"We must wait for the afterbirth," Shifra told them and sat in the rocking chair that Bertha would use in the coming weeks to nurse her baby.

This was how Ida Haberman was born in the year 1915.

2. Kirby Street

Five years ago, Bertha met Yussel Haberman on the Lower East Side of New York. A quiet young man with soft brown eyes and thinning red hair, he had seen her on Orchard Street and fallen in love. Yussel worked as a cutter in a garment loft. He was shorter than Bertha, who was a beauty, though tall at five feet eight inches. At first, she ignored him. He persisted. She gave in. She needed to marry. She was already past twenty. He wasn't bad, she thought.

They moved to Detroit where his relatives had said, "Come. It's good here."

They rented a flat in a two-story yellow wood-sided house on Kirby Street. The owner was Schultz, a German blacksmith who had arrived in Detroit a generation earlier.

Yussel, in partnership with his Uncle Izzy, opened a tailor shop on Mack Avenue, two streetcar rides from the Kirby Street flat.

Each night, Yussel brought Bertha his share of the money from the tailor shop. She kept it in a hatbox in her closet. Nobody knew, not even Yussel.

Ida was born first and then Sarah, eighteen months after. Bertha was a miser and a saver. She and Yussel and the girls wore hand-me-down clothes donated by relatives. The family ate scrawny chicken haggled over by Bertha in the live market on Hastings Street and limp vegetables from the bottom of the crate bought at the Eastern market on Sunday mornings.

For seven years, Ida was already five and Sarah was three, Bertha's hoard slowly grew until one day when Schultz came for the rent, she sat him down with a glass of tea and brought out the hatbox. Times were difficult. Schultz wanted to expand his smithy. Bertha was an implacable negotiator. For twenty-five hundred dollars cash and a note for another twenty-five hundred, payable in seven years at two percent interest, Bertha and Yussel bought the house. None of their relatives knew where the money came from. Bertha wouldn't say. When they yelled at Yussel to tell them, he shrugged and smiled. He wasn't sure himself, but he knew there was no such thing as a sick day.

Then Uncle Izzy vanished with a week's receipts. Bertha and a nephew, Irving, a high school student who was taking business courses, went over the books and slowly discovered that Izzy had been cheating them, taking two dollars for every one taken home by Yussel.

"May he rot in Gehenna," Bertha said, thinking of the wilted vegetables.

Immigrants were still arriving from Eastern Europe. Bertha rented the downstairs flat to a family she knew from her shtetl, the Ginsbergs, educated people and honorable. Marcus, the father, was a scholar who earned a sparse living teaching Hebrew in the Jewish afterschool. He had his share of pride. "Mrs. Haberman, I was born and will die a poor man. I am a loyal member of the Socialist Party. My brethren and I want no more than our rightful portion."

Bertha, preoccupied with family and survival, did not care about socialism. All she knew was that the Ginsbergs would pay their rent. This money, plus the increased profit from Yussel's shop, enabled her to buy better quality vegetables and fatter chickens, sometimes even brisket or a veal roast.

She still put away money into the hatbox every week. She did not know where this money was going to go, but she had no doubt that it would be useful.

The answer came when Bertha received a letter from New York. The envelope was addressed in English. The letter was written in Yiddish. She did not know how to read or write and took it downstairs to her tenant. She listened, entranced, as Marcus Ginsberg read it to her:

Dear Bertha,

This is your sister, Sadie, writing you a letter from New York with the help of a scribe on Grand Street. I have news that will surprise you. Your brother, Michel, who you thought was dead, has come to my flat on Rivington Street. He has had a hard time and talks of nothing but wanting to come to you in Detroit. Bertha, times are bad here, and we have no money to spare. If you can send money, we will buy Michel a train ticket.

We are well here. I hope you are well so far away.

Your loving sister,
Sadie

Bertha wept. Marcus put down the letter and said, "I hope this is not bad news, Mrs. Haberman."

Bertha could not respond. She went up to her flat and rocked in her oak rocking chair. She thought about Michel, the youngest child in her family, and the handsomest, strongest and sunniest of her four brothers. She loved him the most and could not believe he was still alive.

She had last seen him standing in their farmyard with her family. Tossie, the wagoner, had come, his wagon loaded with neighbors who had also decided to go to America. Her father's brother had sent money for one to make the trip. Her father would not leave his farm. The others in her family decided to stay with him. Bertha made the heartbreaking decision to leave alone. Her brothers and sister viewed her as a betrayer. But her father had honored her wish.

When she reached New York, she found a job as a seamstress in a garment loft. She heard the news that Cossacks had come and slaughtered her family and burned down her house. Her neighbors had buried the dead ones. Bertha wept for three days.

She and Yussel welcomed Michel in the Michigan Central depot and brought him to the flat on Kirby Street. He was stooped and wore a suit that was much too big. The girls couldn't help staring despite Bertha's orders to look the other way.

Michel slept on a mattress in the living room. He shut the door at night, but the family could hear his howls. Yussel told Ida that her beloved brother was haunted.

Michel had no appetite. Ida did her best to tempt him with dishes from their childhood, potato latkes, meat-filled knishes, cheese blintzes. He forced himself to swallow, but over the weeks they watched him shrink.

Ida took him to the Woodward Avenue trolley. They rode downtown to the river, sat on a bench and stared at the water, not speaking. At last, she told him that if he was going to kill himself, he had to leave because of the children. Michel told her about the day the Cossacks came. He was away from home, in the village, arranging to sell their grain. When he got back, there was nothing to save. He began to walk west. It took him six years to get to America. And now that he was here, he wanted to go back to the farm.

"You cannot," she said.

"I know," he said. "But there is no life for me in this city."

She grasped his hand and told him that her tenant, Marcus Ginsberg, had talked about a wealthy Jew, Baron de Hirsch, who had been settling poor Jews on farms in the United States and Canada. Marcus will write to Baron de Hirsch, she told him. Michel fainted.

Within three months, he was plowing on his own farm in New Jersey. Bertha's sister, Sadie, and her husband, Hymie, visited him. Sadie wrote to Bertha that Michel was fine and that he was sharing living space with a young woman. Bertha thanked God.

3. Oh, Sister

(Ida Haberman's letter to the Detroit Jewish Chronicle)

Worthy Editor:

My mother says I should bring my sister to the Jewish Center dance. Her cousin told her it would be a mitzvah. Why? My sister can't dance. When we practice the new steps in our living room, she goes into the kitchen. She won't have a thing to wear. And she won't talk to boys, with her eye that doesn't stay straight. I don't see why I have to bring her, even if she is my sister. Please help me with my problem.

Answer: On the one hand, your sister should go to the dance. On the other hand, if she goes, she'll be miserable. And she'll be a burden because you will feel responsible. Bring her to the dance. You have to. And ask some of the boys you are friendly with to dance with her. At least once. What else can you do?

Ida wanted to be a flapper. Oh, how she wanted it. Did she dare? Would Ma let her go to the dance dressed like one of those girls? She conspired with her friends. Nobody else could come into the bedroom.

Natalie helped in a beauty parlor and knew about the flapper bobs. They held their breath when she stood with the scissors poised to cut Ida's long black hair.

Ida closed her eyes. "Oh, God, wait! I can't do it. Oh, God, how can I do it? I can't. I can't. No. Wait. No. Okay, get ready, Natalie. Okay, now do it!"

Natalie snipped. When Ida opened her eyes, she beheld her neck, white and glistening, her hair in heaps around her chair. Deep breaths, but the deed was done. And she couldn't go back. No use worrying about ma now.

Ida opened her J. L. Hudson's box and pulled out a short black dress, a little nothing undergarment (no bra), her stockings that she would roll down and her dancing shoes, white pumps with low heels.

Afloat at the dance. Davy, Harold and Gilbert all admiring, all wanting to dance with her. Ida held out her hands to Gilbert in his white jacket, black tie, shiny black shoes and pimples that he had tried to powder over then gave up.

Danny Schwartz and his Wolverines playing the new Charleston and Ida flying across the floor, hands clapping her knees, hop, hop, hopping across the floor, Gilbert laughing and flailing his arms and matching her hop for hop. And the band never stopping. Danny Schwartz, laughing, encouraging. The other dancers cheering in a circle around them. She could do this all night, never tire, never want to stop.

Another boy brought her a drink. What was in it? Who cared? "Hard stuff from my flask," the boy told a pal.

Ida kept on dancing. The Lindy. The Grizzly Bear. The Cakewalk, high stepping, promenading hand in hand like the old-time slaves imitating high society. First prize, a cake. Ida and Gilbert, laughing until they had to sit on the floor, took the cake!

Another drink. Down the hatch, pally.

Gilbert leading her out to his car. The others sneaking behind to peek.

Gilbert with his arms around her. Ida dizzy. Gilbert kissing her. The horn blows in the car next to them. "Damn," Gilbert says. But the moment is gone. Ida is awake and smacks him. She is out of the car and running to the dance hall. Gilbert is chagrined. The others are laughing.

What a night! So much to talk about the next morning. So much to go over with her gang. But what about Sarah? Ida was supposed to watch out for her little sister.

Drab Sarah, reluctant Sarah, in one of Ida's old dresses with a ribbon in her hair, sat in a corner like Little Miss Muffet and wished that the dance were over before the first trumpet blast.

Punch in the punch bowl and, of course, spiked. Sarah got up once to get a cup of punch, then again and again. Eyes shining now, Sarah went to a shy boy, Rodney, in his stiff, too-big jacket from the Hadassah discount rack, who backed as far as he could in the opposite corner. She dragged him, blushing, to the dance floor. Neither knew the steps. Sarah led him to the punch bowl. Two cups, and that helped. They watched the others and began to do it. A nice fox-trot. One, two, three, four, one, two, three, four, Sarah remembered from watching Ida and her gang in her living room, dancing to the Victrola, Fats Waller, Benny Goodman and the whiz, Louis Armstrong. She had watched and listened behind the kitchen door and wanted to cry. But now enough came to her. Enough. She led Rodney until suddenly, out of the blue, watching the other boys, he began to lead her. And she danced until she forgot that she wasn't pretty.

That morning, Ida, still agog, believing that Sarah wanted to hear everything, was shocked when her sister raved about the band and the great dancing and the nice boy, Rodney.

Their mother, Bertha, in her bedroom, listening, applauded silently. She told herself, "Hey, you never know."

4. Sammy

Sammy Gottlieb was Sadie's son and Bertha's nephew. He was helping to organize the construction workers in New York City. Tom O'Rourke, a contractor, hated the unions and was Sam's particular enemy. Tom planned for a fatal accident in his factory.

Natalie Finn worked in Tom's office. She was blond, pretty, a little hefty and fated for fat motherhood, but that was years away. Meanwhile, she was having fun with all those men around. Sammy, who was in and out of Tom's office for rancorous meetings, wondered why other men didn't understand what he did: how to make women fall for him. It was so easy. He had the knack, inborn. A certain smile, a stillness inside, a way of listening, a way of letting them come to him, thinking it was their doing, their choice, that he was willing putty.

Natalie warned Sammy. A few days later, a steel beam fell on Tom's head. Sammy and Natalie were twenty-five blocks uptown in a hotel room. When she heard the news, Natalie went upstate to live in a yellow house with her mother.

The union president, Morris Hillquit, was planning to run for mayor of New York City and thought it best for Sam to disappear. Hillquit talked with Sam's mother, a veteran of the picket lines and a realist. Sadie, came up with the solution: Detroit.

"Mom, they're sending me away."

"I know, Sam."

"Why? Why are they doing that?"

"I told them to do it."

"What? Mom!"

"Sam, you need a fresh start."

"No, I don't."

"You do. And going to Detroit will help. You'll see."

"What makes you think I'll be better off there?"

"Detroit is not New York. There are not so many distractions. You'll be with my sister, Bertha, and her Yussel, and their two little girls."

"Little girls?"

"Your cousins."

"I don't want to go, Mom."

"I know, but you have to. Things here are not good for you. And Mr. Hillquit will find you a union job. He has friends."

"He already said they might want me to help organize the dressmakers."

"So see? He has something in mind for you."

"Are there dressmakers in Detroit"?

"There must be."

"I'm in trouble here?"

"I think so."

"Okay, I'll go."

Cold, freezing cold and endless snow on the ground and more coming. Sammy figured that Detroit must be near the North Pole, but he was ready with his heavy duffel coat, long red scarf, leather gloves, fedora, earmuffs and galoshes. He toted two big suitcases. Following directions that Sadie wrote for him, he rode the yellow clanging streetcar from downtown Detroit to Kirby Street and the Haberman house. He rang the bell, clumped up the stairs to Bertha's kitchen of good smells and looked at his family that he had never met: his stout, graying-haired, welcoming aunt and two cousins who were excited and curious, and not so little, and certainly didn't consider themselves as such.

Whoa. He wasn't ready for them.

"Sammy, we didn't know when you were coming." Bertha was stirring a big pot with a wooden spoon. The smell was wonderful. Chicken soup. He was starving.

They stared at him, a big man over six feet tall with broad shoulders, handsome with rippling red hair and loud. He shouted at them. "You must be my cousins, Ida and Sarah. My mom said you were little."

Ida, perky, full-bodied, a dark-haired beauty, said, "We used to be, Cousin Sammy. Sarah is still littler than I am."

"What? Are you both in high school or something?"

"Cousin Sammy." Sarah was approaching with her hand out. "I'm in the tenth grade." Her voice was deep. One of her eyes moved oddly, out of step. He handed her his coat, hat and scarf and sat to take off his galoshes, leaving pools of water on Bertha's spotless floor.

He pointed to his suitcases. "Where should I put these, Aunt Bertha?"

"I'll get them," Sarah said from the hallway where she was hanging Sam's things. Without being told, she set Sam's suitcases on newspapers in the hall at the head of the stairs and mopped the wet places. Ida limited herself to smiling at Sam and small talk. "How was your trip, Cousin Sammy? Are you hungry? Wait'll you taste my mom's chicken soup."

"Okay, yes, and I can't wait," he answered, watching Sarah accomplish her tasks while his Aunt Bertha pulled a roasting pan out of the oven, using her apron as a pot holder.

"Don't starve, Sammy," Bertha told him. "Yussel comes from his store. We'll eat soon. Go wash up."

"Wash off that New York grime, Cousin Sammy," Ida advised.

He nodded at her and smiled. *Not bad for Detroit*, he thought.

"Come, I'll show you the bathroom, Cousin Sam." Sarah took his hand and led him out of the kitchen. He was charmed and admired her slender back, not quite womanly. He considered himself an expert on such matters. He said, "I have beautiful cousins."

"Hah." She shrugged. "One anyway."

An opening Sammy never would resist. "Two, Sarah. You don't know it yet."

She stiffened and did not answer.

In the kitchen, Yussel arrived, a full head shorter than Sam and chortling, "Hoo, hoo, hoo," at the size of Bertha's nephew.

In New York, Sammy's father, Hymie, also a union veteran, was stubborn, an idealist, certainly not a realist. His latest fiasco was an attempt to organize the hat-makers. Hymie, though he would not admit it to himself, planned for failure. He was persuasive and led the hat-making men and women into a strike without the support of Mr. Hillquit who didn't have time for doomed ventures. Hymie returned home to lick his wounds. Sadie was not sympathetic. Hands on hips, she had warned him. Sammy had seen this whole attempt to fight the bosses unravel before and was disgusted. When Mr. Hillquit talked of Detroit and the dressmakers, Sammy saw his chance to outshine Hymie. And maybe if they came his way, girls. Why not?

Bertha's dinner that first night consisted of chicken soup with matzo balls, roast chicken, potatoes cooked in the same pan, knishes, kreplach, canned peas, a big challah bread, and bottles of seltzer and Vernor's Ginger Ale. For dessert, she had made a prune and apricot stew. "So you don't get bound up," she explained.

Sammy lectured them. "If you're going to fight the bosses, you have to be smart." He talked about the need to plan, to line up support of friendly unions, to build a strike fund and, above all, to educate the workers about their rights and the bosses' willingness to starve their children.

As he chewed and made appreciative noises over Bertha's roast chicken and browned potatoes, he watched his cousins. Ida did not take her eyes off him. She was trying out her feminine techniques: unexpected sighs, knowing little smiles. She wanted him to watch her. Sam was content. He had seen this before. He had seen the deep breaths that made her breasts swell and push out her blouse. He knew that he could play with her. Toward what end? He shook his head. She was, after all, his first cousin, family. Ah, well.

Sarah was another matter. She was busy helping Bertha, carrying platters, clearing plates. She seemed unaware of him, which experience told him was not possible. Still, she was locked away, far from flirtation. Definitely, definitely she interested him. Sammy took pride in solving challenges.

Four old wooden desks, a wall of file cabinets, two girls punching away at typewriters, and the name on the door of the fourth-floor office, Marcus Rosen, Regional Director, AF of L. Sammy carried a letter from Morris Hillquit.

Rosen, short, red-headed, bearded, pipe-smoking, read the letter and glared at Sammy. "Are you a New York wiseass?"

Sam was pleased. "Sure."

Rosen was disgusted. "Morris Hillquit wants me to give you an organizing job."

Sam did his humble act. "I just want to fit in, help if I can."

"Skip the bullshit." Rosen was reaching for a file. He turned to one of the typists. "Queenie."

In her fifties and stout, Queenie swiveled in her chair and recognized Sammy as a man who liked women. Sammy looked at her and couldn't help smiling. It was like a meeting of old friends.

Rosen saw them and was unhappy. Queenie knew, but didn't care. Sammy, as usual, was unaware of other men.

Rosen had an "important" assignment. The dressmaking companies had been playing off the gentile local against the Jewish local; whichever came up with the sweetest package would be awarded the contract. This had been going on for ten years. Sammy was to go to the American Union of Dressmakers, the gentile local, and begin a negotiation that would reconcile them with their Jewish counterparts.

"I can do it," Sammy said.

"Good," Rosen smiled.

"Damn fool," Queenie said.

"I'll see you later," Sammy told her.

Over beer, she wised him up. "Our Jewish local can't agree on anything. The Communists hate the Socialists, and they both hate the Zionists. They're paralyzed. Nothing gets done here."

"What about Rosen?"

"Him? He's nothing. Just an American Jew. That's why they made him president."

"I'll still go to the goyim."

"Your funeral, pal."

Sunday morning, Ida went out for bagels, lox and cream cheese and saw four policemen sitting in the police car in front of their house. The motor was running, no doubt to keep them warm. The policemen looked at her. She smiled at them. They did not smile back. She became frightened and walked quickly to Hastings Street and the store. When she returned, the police car was still there. The policemen looked at her again. She ran to the house, up the stairs and into the kitchen, trying not to cry.

Sammy was not surprised. "They followed me."

Yussel was upset. "What are they doing here? This is America," he said in Yiddish.

Sammy answered in Yiddish. "Even in America the police oppress the little man."

Sarah was setting the table. She was indignant. "But you haven't done anything."

"I'm here," Sammy said, sounding important. "That's enough."

Yussel scowled at his coffee. "Gonifs. I'll picket."

"You'll have a chance to do that, Uncle Yussel," Sammy said.

Sarah was excited. "You're organizing a strike, Sammy?"

Sammy patted her hand. "You going to march with us, cousin?"

Sarah drew a deep breath. "People should not be oppressed. I'll march."

There were twelve of them in a semicircle, heavy coats hung on the backs of the chairs. Cigarette and cigar smoke layered the room. Sammy sat facing them. He took a deep breath. "You may have heard of Morris Hillquit," he said. "He and Debs formed the Socialist Party in America. Guys, Mr. Hillquit sent me here to talk with you. He wants you to make peace with the Jewish local. I can speak for them. We are proposing that you combine with the Jewish workers so that you can force the bosses to give you a living wage. What do you think? Do you want me to shut up or keep talking?"

He talked for forty-five minutes about his vision of a strong combined union. He loved to feel persuasive, to move men to collective action. They listened and told him that they would consider and let him know. Sammy was solemn, containing his excitement. This was the high spot of his trip to Detroit.

Of course, they had heard it before. Make peace with the Jews? There weren't enough jobs as it was. What did they care about Hillquit?

He waited, finally telephoned. They said that they were still discussing it.

It took him a while to understand that Rosen had sent him on a fool's errand, that he had been set up to fail.

Detroit winters made Ida suffer, and not just from the penetrating cold which passed easily through her sweaters, scarves, boots, mittens and wool hats to so chill her flesh and bones that it took hours in a heated house with radiators hissing to warm up. More than the cold, and even worse because of what it did to her soul, was the gray depressing winterlong light filtered by low clouds that sat on the tops of the houses. Where was the sun? What did it matter? When it managed to find a path through the clouds, the sunlight, exhausted by the effort, fell uselessly, a pale and sickly yellowish glow, upon snow dirtied by coal dust from the house chimneys, upon snow mountains heaped up at the street intersections and the two- and three-feet-high mounds shoveled onto the lawns along both sides of the sidewalks.

The walk down Kirby Street straight into the wind was the worst. Ida turned her back to the wind, glancing over her shoulder, taking small steps. She tried to watch for other people, but had to stop when a voice called out, "Hey, miss, be careful there."

Ida turned and confronted a tall young man wearing a thin coat and a cap, sporting a long blue-knitted scarf that reached almost to the sidewalk. He was staring at her. He looked angry.

Ida said, "Excuse me," and started to pass him. But he moved at the same time, and the two of them were still face-to-face. She moved the other way, and so did he.

She stared. He bowed and swept out an arm, indicating that she should proceed while he stood still. As she passed him, darting a puzzled glance, he said, "Good evening, Miss Haberman."

Ida stopped and looked up at him. "I beg your pardon?"

"You're wondering if we've met," he said. "We haven't." He seemed angry again and said nothing more.

What an irritating man, Ida decided. She shrugged and walked away.

When she had taken a few steps, he called out, "How's your cousin Sam?"

She whirled to face him. "What?"

"You know," he said, "your cousin Sam, the Communist agitator."

Ida was flabbergasted. "What? What?"

He stepped close to her. "I'm Sergeant Boylan," he said. "With the Detroit police."

She stepped back. "What? The police?"

He said, "We're interested in the red cell you people are part of."

Ida felt faint. "What? What are you talking about?"

Sergeant Boylan was no longer polite or friendly. "Tell your cousin Sam," he shouted at her, "that he should go back to Jew York with the rest of his Commie friends. We don't want Commie kikes like him here in Detroit."

"Oh, my God!" Ida screamed. She raced to her house and ran up the steps to the flat. She flung open the door. Her mother was getting dinner ready. Ida sobbed out her story to Bertha and Sarah.

That night, the family conferred. Sammy told them that he would move out.

"What!" Bertha threw up her arms. "Never."

"I can stay with union friends," he said. "It would be better."

Yussel banged the table with his fist. In Yiddish he said, "You don't leave us, Shmuel. We are your blood family. You don't go away from us."

Sammy was grim. "They're going to frighten you as long as I'm here."

Ida was crying again. Sarah said, "Let them. Stay. Don't go."

Sammy said, "Ida, are you frightened? Do you want me to leave?"

Ida shook her head and said that she didn't feel good and wanted to go to bed. She sobbed and left the kitchen.

Sammy stood. "I've got to go. It's not fair to her."

Bertha said, "Nischt, nischt, nischt. You stay."

Yussel said, "A chalaria on them."

Sarah walked to Sammy. She held his hands. "You'll stay. You can't leave us."

Sammy said, "Look at what's happening. How can I stay?"

Bertha said, "What would Hymie and Sadie say?"

Sammy grinned. "They would say to stay."

"So?" Yussel said. "That's the answer."

Nine o'clock the next evening, the phone rang. Sarah answered. "What!" she said in a loud voice. The others gathered around. "Sammy! What! No!"

"Vus, vus?" Bertha said.

Sarah shook her head, listening, her lips moving silently, her eyes wide. "When? When is it? Tomorrow morning! My God, Sammy." She hung up.

"I can't stand it," she told them. "That was Sammy."

"We know," Ida shouted.

"He's in jail," Sarah said. Now the keeper of Sammy's flame, she was in despair.

"Mein Gott." Bertha collapsed onto a chair and buried her face in her hands.

Yussel, who had not spoken, went to the closet and took out his coat and hat.

"Pa," Ida shouted, "where are you going?"

"To the police," Yussel said. "I'm going to Sammy."

"Pa," Ida pleaded. "You can't do any good."

Bertha said, "Yussel, du bist mishuga."

"Sha," he said. "Sammy needs me."

Sarah said, "Pa, where are you going? You don't know where the jail is."

Yussel hesitated.

She said, "Pa, we don't where he is. How can you find him?"

Yussel sat at the kitchen table. "In America," he said, "it shouldn't happen."

"His hearing is tomorrow morning," Sarah said. "He said not to worry."

"Hearing?" Bertha said.

"With a judge," Sarah answered.

"A judge," Bertha said. "Mein Gott."

Yussel was indignant. "A chalaria on the judge. A chalaria on America."

"No, Pa," Sarah said. "Don't curse America."

Yussel wouldn't calm down. "The czar and his police are in America."

Bertha said, "Sammy is a good boy. They wouldn't keep him in jail."

Sarah said again, "He said not to worry. He'll be fine."

Bertha went to the stove. "Pot roast," she said. "It shouldn't go to waste. I'll save some for Sammy."

He arrived the next afternoon and sat at the table looking weary. The family was out except for Sarah who had come home from school. She brought him coffee. "We didn't know when you were coming, Sammy."

He sighed and shook his head. "The union got me a good lawyer. Otherwise . . ."

Sarah was teary-eyed. "What happened? Why did they arrest you?"

"They arrested me for loitering."

"Loitering?"

He explained that he had been talking with his friends on Hastings Street. "Not doing anything. Just talking."

"How could they?"

He told her about police harassment. "They think I'm a dangerous person. They want me to leave Detroit." He laughed angrily. "I told them I just got here."

Sarah cried out. "Oh, Sammy, I'm afraid for you."

He smiled broadly. "I told them nothing is going to make me leave my little cousin Sarah."

"You told them my name!"

He put his big hand over hers. "They know all of your names, sweetheart."

"No."

"Sorry. You're on their list."

She was indignant. "Whose list? What list?"

"The police," he said. "They keep a list of dangerous radicals. Look out front and see if the police car is back."

Sarah ran to the living room. She was back in an instant, nodding unhappily. "They saw me looking at them." She waved her fists in the air.

"What a family!" he said. "What a cousin!" He jumped up. "Come here." He held out his arms, smiling, inviting.

For a moment, Sarah hesitated. She wanted to fling herself into Sammy's arms, but at the same time, the impulse frightened her.

Arms still spread, Sammy beckoned with his fingers, insisting.

"Sammy," she murmured and ran to him. He hugged her and kissed her cheek. "What a family. What a cousin," he said again. He let her go and stepped back.

"Sammy," Sarah said in a soft voice that she did not recognize as being her own. "I'm so glad you came to us."

"Yeah." Sammy was suddenly gloomy. "You might be the only ones."

Sarah had the sensation of seeing Sammy the warrior replaced by an uncertain and vulnerable young man. She wanted to hug him. "Oh, Sammy. Why?"

"It's all a bad joke, Sarah. If the police knew, they would laugh. I don't know what to do."

She watched him and waited. He began to pace the kitchen. He told her that he had never seen anything like it, that his friends were more interested in fighting each other than in fighting the bosses. "The Jewish union can't agree on anything. They hate the goyish union and vice versa. The labor movement here is impossible. I don't have a real job here. What a mess. Sarah! You know what?"

She was breathing deeply, remembering his arms around her and happy that he was confiding what had to be his secret business. "What?"

"I'm going to take a shower." He left the kitchen, calling out, "What a mess!"

Sarah heard the bathroom door close and the shower running. For a moment, she allowed herself to think about Sammy in the shower and pictured the water running down his tall body. She picked up the coffee cups and put them in the sink, but could not run the hot water while he was in the shower. She had an impulse to look at herself in the mirror and decided to go to her room. Outside of the bathroom, she heard him singing. He could not carry a tune. For the briefest moment, she thought about him soaping his private parts, shivered, and walked into her room. She decided not to look at herself, afraid that, as always, she would see a plain girl, not pretty enough for him. Sarah walked to the kitchen. Before she got there, she heard the bathroom door open and looked back. Sammy was standing in the hall wrapped in a big towel. She felt herself blush, felt weak in the legs. He was smiling. "That was nice. Now I'm hungry."

"There's pot roast from last night," she told him.

"Perfect," he said. "I'll put on clean clothes. Eat pot roast. And I'll be ready for this crazy city."

Sammy drank his third cup of coffee. Sarah put the dishes into the sink. He watched her. "You always do the dishes?"

Sarah nodded. "If Ida washed them, I'd have to do them over again."

"And you clean the house?" he said.

"Every day," Sarah said. "After school."

"And where is Ida?"

"With her friends."

"I see." Sammy was serious. "Sit a moment. I want to tell you a story."

Sarah knew what was coming. "You're going to tell me that I'm an oppressed worker."

"Sit, please," he said.

She sat across from him, smiling slightly, sipping her coffee.

Sammy told her about girls in 1909 who worked for the shirtwaist bosses and were suffering from low wages and terrible long hours. "And listen to this, Sarah." He covered her hand with his as if to protect against the vision of bosses and the shop foremen. "The bastards chose the pretty ones and did what they wanted to them. Do you understand?" He was concerned for her sensibilities.

She, of course, knew exactly what he was saying. "The girls couldn't help themselves?"

"Not if they wanted to keep their jobs."

Sarah groaned. "That was terrible."

"Terrible." Sammy was indignant. "But some of the girls, a few, decided to fight back." His eyes were shining. "They tried to strike, Sarah, but they weren't organized."

"My God. What happened?"

Sammy told her that the girls tried and tried, and failed and failed, until there was a big meeting at the Cooper's Union. "Thousands were in the hall. Samuel Gompers spoke."

"I've heard of him," Sarah said.

"A great labor leader," he said. "I was named after him."

"Oh, Sammy."

"Gompers spoke. Others spoke." He described the uncertainty of the union leaders who didn't know how far the girls were prepared to go. "That's when Clara Lemlich, a skinny girl, who was sitting there all day, ran up to the podium and said, 'I am one of those striking against intolerable conditions. I am tired of listening to speakers who talk in generalities. What we are here for is to decide whether or not to strike. I offer a resolution that a general strike be declared. Now.'"

"Oh, Sammy." Sarah was teary-eyed.

"The place went crazy," he said. "The next day, the girls, all of them, thousands, went out on strike."

"And they won the strike."

"Not everything. It wasn't so simple." He told her that Mrs. Belmont and Miss Morgan gave money and that Gompers and the AF of L supported the girls, but the owners wouldn't give in. "The strike went on for weeks and weeks. The girls and their families suffered. But they held together. Finally the bosses settled."

"The girls won?"

"They got more money, shorter hours and respect for their womanhood. And most important, the union held together because one little girl stuck up for her rights."

"You think I should strike," Sarah said.

"I don't see why you do all the work, and Ida gets off doing nothing."

Sarah sighed. "Sometimes," she said, "that's just the way things are. I really don't mind."

"You should mind," Sammy said. "It's wrong."

"It's the way Ma wants it."

"She has no right."

Sarah touched his hand to emphasize the importance of what she was telling him. "She has. She works as hard as I do. She helps Pa. She depends on me."

"While Ida has it easy?"

"Yes." Sarah looked at him steadily. "That's the way it is. Ida is the beautiful princess. I am the ugly scullery maid."

"Sarah," Sammy said. "What are you talking about?"

She bit her lip. "It's true."

"Sarah," he said, putting his hands on her shoulders.

"Sammy," she wept, "don't touch me. It isn't right."

He pulled her close. "You are beautiful," he said.

Sarah was gulping. "No, what are you saying? What are you doing?"

He kissed her. She swayed. He held her up and led her to the bedroom.

I'm glad to be back on the train. Going home. Where I belong.

Ma, he said I was beautiful.

She was too young. I shouldn't have done it.

Ma, I'm going to stay in bed for a while. No, I'm okay. I just want to be in bed.

I had to leave. It wasn't going forward like it should have.

Sammy, I'll never forget you. They keep asking me what's wrong.

I'll tell Mr. Hillquit, "I'm sorry, sir. It was hopeless in Detroit. They weren't ready."

Sammy, I can't look at Ma. Ida is looking at me funny.

The family will never figure it out. How can they imagine what happened?

Ida says the police car is gone.

She'll be okay.

Sammy, how can I go on living?

It was a nice moment.

Sammy, I'll come to you in New York.

She'll forget. Time heals. I know.

Sammy, why did you leave?

I know, I know. I shouldn't have done it. I let myself get carried away. Again. I know it. It happened again. But it's not the end of the world, is it?

No, Ma, I can't explain. I just don't feel right. I want to stay in bed. Ida will help you. No, Ma, I don't know what's wrong. I have to stay in bed . . . for now . . . Sammy . . .

So long, Sarah.

5. Satisfaction

A heavy snow fell during the night. In the clear, cold morning, men were shoveling the sidewalks, heads down, snow was flying. Scrapers lifted the ice and hard-packed snow. Drivers cranked their cars. A Model T Ford backfired. A car raced its back wheels against drifted snow. A burnt rubber smell wafted. The driver kept spinning his wheels. Shovelers stopped and watched, shaking their heads, grinning. Still the driver persisted, sinking his car deeper and deeper. At last, red-faced, he jumped out of his car and kicked it.

Ida, nodding to neighbors, smiling, dodging shovels, was on her way to Hastings Street, shopping for Ma. She almost collided with the young Irish cop who had yelled at her when Sammy came to them.

"We meet again, Ms. Haberman." Unbelievably, he was friendly and smiling, tugging at his cap with red hands.

She stared at him. "What do you want?"

Wasting a smile, he said, "Do you remember me? I'm Sergeant Boylan."

She glared at him and continued on her way. He turned and kept pace with her. She snapped, "Why are you walking with me? I don't need your company."

He said, "I just wanted to tell you that your cousin, Sam, did the smart thing, leaving Detroit. He was going to make trouble for you and your family."

She stopped. "Why are you telling me this? What do you want?"

He nodded. "I understand how you feel, Ms. Haberman. I'm sure you and your family are decent Americans."

"Really? Were you thinking of arresting us and putting us in jail?" She had wanted to wither him. But to herself, she sounded girlish and shrill. She hated her voice.

He smiled. "Of course not." He reached out and touched her arm. "Actually, I'm off duty now."

She shook off his hand. "Really?" That was better. Her voice was low and sarcastic. "Then what do you want? Why are you bothering me?"

He looked like the shy boys in her school. "Actually, Ms. Haberman, I haven't come to bother you. But you know, you are very pretty."

Ida felt herself blushing. *My God, I can't believe it.* She had the sensation of wanting her legs to resume their strides and of her legs refusing to move themselves. She gasped, "What are you talking about?"

He pulled off his cap and fumbled with the brim, speaking quietly now. "Well, I just wondered if you would like to go out on a date with me?"

"What!" Ida thought about writing to Sammy about this conversation. Whoever heard of such a thing? "Never." She was shrill again. "Are you kidding me?"

He persisted in his low voice. "You know, I was doing my duty when I talked to you like that. They told me to upset you. I was just following orders."

Ida suddenly stepped forward, almost bumping him. "Listen you, you get away from me."

He looked hurt. "Now, Ms. Haberman, that's no way to be."

She had him on the run and loved the feeling. "If you don't leave me alone, Sergeant Boylan, I will call police headquarters and complain about you."

He backed away. "Okay, okay. Don't get so excited."

"And I'll tell them you asked me for a date."

He put on his cap and tugged it low over his eyes. His voice was cold with rage. "Maybe you're just a little kike bitch after all."

He walked away rapidly. Ida continued to the stores. She could not remember what Ma had told her to buy. Fortunately, she realized she had a list.

6. Sarah and Josh

Sarah Haberman was selling shoes in the second basement of J. L. Hudson's. In came a young man with two little girls. He was polite and neatly dressed. She noted that the three of them were fair-skinned and blond. Not Jewish, she figured, until he told her that the two little girls were going to a family bar mitzvah and needed dress-up shoes.

Oops, she thought, *blonde Jews* and said, "Please sit, and I'll measure them."

When she brought samples for their inspection, the girls squirmed in their chairs and whispered to the young man.

"They like the black patent leather shoes with the strap."

"Mary Janes." Sarah smiled. "They may be a little expensive. Three ninety-five a pair."

He made a face and said okay. The girls were thrilled and hugged him. They padded self-consciously up and down the carpeted floor in their new shoes.

"Would you like to see your feet in the shoes?" Sarah asked and led the way to the x-ray machine. Peering into the viewer, the awed girls could see the bones of their feet; they scrunched their toes and giggled.

"That was nice of you," the man said as Sarah filled out the bill. He looked at her closely, making her uncomfortable. Too late, she turned so that he could not see her right eye. He said, "My name is Josh Greenberg."

Sarah didn't respond. Years ago, rather than torturing herself over what could not be, she had chosen to accept what she saw in the mirror: a girl who was not pretty and, worse, whose right eye wandered. Actually, over time, for whatever reasons of practice and maturation, her bad eye often moved in step with its partner. But that was long after it would do any good for her self-esteem. Now she looked in surprise at Josh Greenberg who was husky, with a straight nose and blue-gray eyes, his hair combed to the sides of his part. What could he want with her? She put the shoeboxes into a big Hudson's bag and put his bill on top of the boxes. "If you want to return these, Mr. Greenberg, you'll need the receipt."

He seemed a little nervous. "You haven't told me your name."

Again she did not answer.

He let out a breath. "Okay, kids, let's go."

One of the little girls smiled at Sarah and said, "We live on Ferry."

"Really," Sarah said. "I live on Kirby. What's your address?"

Neither of the girls knew. Josh Greenberg told her. And Sarah couldn't help telling him, "I live on the same block, right behind you."

He whistled at the coincidence and asked a third time for her name. She reasoned that she could not be so impolite to a neighbor, blushed, and told him. He thanked her and asked if he could phone her. She was amazed and looked at the girls. He laughed and told her that he was their uncle. She gave him her phone number. He called the next day, and they agreed to go to the movie on Saturday evening. She instructed him to wait for her outside of her house.

It was not unusual for Sarah to go to the movies with her friends. Her mother, who was in the kitchen and could hear the phone conversation, had no idea that her daughter was talking to a man. Though on that Saturday evening, she was aware that Sarah was taking longer than usual with the new pageboy hairdo that her older sister, Ida, had told them was all the rage and that her plain daughter had rouged her cheeks. "Wouldn't help," Bertha muttered to herself.

Sarah almost never had dates unless Ida fixed her up because she wanted another couple along or because their mother had been pushing her. Sarah had no skill at boy-girl talk. Ida jabbered away, laughing and teasing. Sarah managed single-word responses. She couldn't wait for the night to end.

That Saturday evening, she simply put on her coat and informed her mother that she would not be late. Outside, she breathed a sigh of relief. She did not realize that Ida, who was coming home, had seen her walking down the block with a young man. And Ida couldn't wait to drop this news into her mother's lap.

Josh took Sarah to the nearby Avalon Theater to see *Bombshell* with Jean Harlow, and afterward to Cunningham's for ice cream sodas. They talked about the movie. He liked it. She wasn't sure if it was nice for her to admit that she liked the Harlow character. "I don't know, she was very brassy."

"It was Jean Harlow," he said and laughed. She did too and then couldn't get over the sensation of laughing with a man. She felt unreal and thought she must be dreaming. She wondered if she had a funny expression on her face, because he looked at her closely and patted her hand. He led them into a discussion of the weather, the flavors of ice cream sodas they liked, and he told her about his job. He was a draftsman at an architectural firm on West Grand Boulevard in the Fisher Building.

Sarah had been in the Fisher Building. Who hadn't, with its beautiful deco lobby and the gorgeous Fisher movie theater? They talked about friends who were out of work. Sarah told him that her salary had been reduced from twenty-one to eighteen dollars a week plus her commission of five or six dollars. He said he made about the same. She told him that she was the best salesperson in her department and that she was the only one who was smart enough to take care of three or four customers at the same time. He said he wasn't surprised. She reasoned that they were about the same age. Why wasn't he attached? She hadn't a clue.

Outside of her home, he said, "I had a nice time."

Sarah was overwhelmed. She could only blush and bob her head in agreement. Didn't her bad eye bother him?

He said, "Can we do it again? Next Saturday night?"

She nodded and ran into the house, past her aggravated mother who called out, "Nu?" and straight to her bedroom. She threw herself on the bed, stared at the ceiling and waited for her heart to stop thumping. When she felt calmer, she emerged to join her mother in the kitchen. Bertha, who was blunt in confrontations with her children, said, "So you're sneaking out of the house to meet a man."

Sarah sank into a chair, covered her face and said, "Oh, no. Oh, God."

Bertha, a tall, bulky woman, had arrived from the old country twenty years ago. Her face was square and strong. There were still traces of a beautiful girl in her small nose and regular features. The way she looked, the way she moved and carried herself, so upright, with such certainty, conveyed forcefulness. Her husband, Yussel, a sweet-natured tailor, brought home his earnings and had nothing to say about running the household. His pleasure at home was to read the Yiddish newspaper, the Forvertz, out loud to Bertha.

Now that she had been discovered, Sarah knew that her mother would want to know everything about how this miracle had happened. Bertha was indulgent with her older daughter, Ida, who was pretty and smart enough to tell her mother more details about her dates than Bertha cared to hear. But Sarah did not want to be questioned. She hardly understood herself what had taken place. She would not discuss her date except to tell her mother Josh's name, that he lived behind them on Ferry, that they had gone to the movie and had ice cream sodas and that she was going to see him again next Saturday evening. She would not reveal what Josh looked like, how they met or what kind of work he did. All Sarah knew was that they had had a nice time and were comfortable over ice cream sodas. She needed nothing more than that and did not want to betray the fact that she was excited about seeing him again and that she could not, in her heart, fathom why he liked her. Moreover, she was worried that to expose her doubts would somehow endanger her new friendship.

That wouldn't do for Bertha. Sarah knew she sounded defensive. "Ma, what do you want from me? There's nothing to tell."

"You went with this man to the movie?"

"Yes."

"And for ice cream sodas?"

"Yes, Ma."

Bertha was angry. "Sarah, that's it?"

"What do mean 'that's it'?"

"You don't know him. You don't know about these things. Bring him to the house."

"What for?"

"So I can meet your boyfriend."

"Ma! He's not my boyfriend!"

Bertha, when she chose to, could wither Sarah with an implacable glare. "You heard me. I don't want to hear anything more from you."

Sarah would not let her mother see her cry, so she went back to her room.

Ida, who had a pack of girlfriends and all the boys in the world, was jealous. She sat on Sarah's bed and admired herself in the mirror while she talked. "Ma won't put up with it."

Sarah was hugging a pillow. "What are you talking about? Put up with what? I haven't done anything."

Ida turned her head, trying to study her profile. "Sarah, I don't mean to hurt your feelings, but you know you don't attract boys."

Sarah rubbed her right eye. "We liked each other." The words sounded dumb, inadequate. Sarah herself was not convinced. She said in a whisper, "Why isn't that enough, Ida?"

Ida shook her head to convey sympathy for her stricken sister. "Well, you know, there must be something wrong with him, Sarah."

Sarah tried to remember how she felt when Josh walked her home. She said, "No. I don't know. He's nice."

Ida said, "So if he's okay, you have no reason not to bring him to the house." Sarah did not know how to respond.

Saturday evening, she brought Josh up to her flat. "Sure," he had agreed. "I'm a stranger who likes their daughter. They want to know about me."

"Too good to be true," Sarah worried. In a mechanical voice, she introduced Josh to her mother and Ida and sat like a stone in an overstuffed chair.

Conversation was up to Josh who quietly explained that until a year ago, he had lived with his parents in Toledo, Ohio, when they were killed in an auto accident. Now he lived with his uncle and aunt on Ferry and was starting a new life.

"Oy," Bertha said and made an involuntary sign with the little finger and forefinger of both hands that was believed in her old shtetl in the Ukraine to keep away misfortune.

Josh nodded. "I am single. I have a steady job. And I am happy that I have met Sarah."

Ida said, "Have you dated any other girls in Detroit, Mr. Greenberg?"

"Ida!" Sarah said. "You have no right."

"Sorry, Sarah," Ida said, biting her lip and looking girlish. "I just naturally couldn't help wondering. That's the way I happen to be, Mr. Greenberg. Cards on the table, you know."

Josh drew a deep breath. "I have been grieving."

He sat quietly, looking at the Habermans' oriental carpet with its tan and pink rosettes and gray border. Bertha stared at him. Sarah thought her mother was trying to divine some secret about Josh that was masked by his calm acceptance of their doubts about him.

Her cheeks glowing with embarrassment and sympathy for him, Sarah stood and said, "Can we go, Ma? We'll be late for the movie."

"Gae, gae, gazint," Bertha muttered.

"Go with good fortune," Sarah translated as they walked down the stairs.

"I know what that meant," Josh said, and he added, "Your mother doesn't trust me."

"Why do you say that?" Sarah said.

"I could tell," Josh said. He looked gloomy. "Cards on the table."

"Oh, Josh," Sarah said and took his arm.

In the Habermans' living room, Bertha and Ida compared opinions.

"He seemed nice," Ida said.

Bertha shook her head. "Something is wrong."

"What, Ma? That he likes Sarah? What's wrong with that?" Ida knew the answer to that question. She and her mother had long since concluded that Sarah was doomed to spinsterhood, that she was the ugly duckling. It was unbelievable to them that a nice-looking man like Josh could want to spend the evening with Sarah, particularly now that he had met Ida.

Bertha shook her head. "It's not that. It's his color."

"His color?"

"He had color in his face." She touched her own pale cheeks. "No good. No good."

"What do you mean, Ma?"

"You'll see," Bertha said. "You'll see." And then she added mysteriously, "Even in America."

For her part, Sarah was having trouble with her feet; they did not seem to be touching the ground. Perplexed, Sarah feared that without her hand clinging to Josh's arm she would soar into the clouds. She wondered if he could read her mind. She wanted to be hidden safely in the dark movie theater. "What's playing?" she asked.

He seemed distracted. "*Golddiggers of 1933*."

"Oh, good," she said. "I love Ginger Rogers. I love her dancing."

He said, "Maybe we should just get something to eat. There's a White Castle on Davidson." Sounding sad, he added, "We could talk."

Sarah was still holding his arm. "If you say so." What could he want to talk about? She was dizzy with the feeling that Josh liked her, but maybe was about to take away her happiness. "Please," she murmured a silent prayer. She said, "I'll pay my share."

He shrugged. "Five cents for a hamburger, three cents for a coffee. I'll pretend I'm Rockefeller."

They ordered, sitting quietly at the counter. The counterman, in his white apron and cap, handed them mugs of coffee. They both added cream, two spoons of sugar and stirred. The silence made her nervous. "I hope you weren't offended by Ida."

"No."

"She thinks she can say anything she wants."

He smiled. "I could see that."

"I'm sure my ma liked you."

He shook his head. "It doesn't matter, Sarah."

She felt frightened. "What do you mean?"

Their hamburgers arrived. He bit into his and sipped his coffee. "I didn't tell your mother the truth. I think she suspected that."

Sarah had a sinking feeling. "What do you mean?"

"The last two years, I wasn't in Toledo. I was in Denver."

She stared at him, baffled. "What?"

"At the National Jewish Hospital for TB."

She gasped. "You have TB?"

"I did. They think that I'm cured now, Sarah. Really."

Sarah covered her face with her hands. "Josh . . ." she mourned. She knew that there was no chance that her mother would allow her to marry a boy who had had tuberculosis, never mind that he said he was cured. Nobody in this day and age could believe that. And what was worse, she knew that he had to have known that a family like hers, that a mother like hers, would never permit it. Not in a million years. He knew and had allowed her to begin to believe in him, to begin to doubt the fate that she had learned to accept.

Josh sounded like he was in pain. "Do you want to go home?"

Sarah screamed at him. "I can't stand it. You tricked me."

"Let's go." Josh left money on the counter.

All the way home she had trouble lifting her feet from the sidewalk. Later, sleepless in her bed, thrashing her legs under the quilt, she could not get his parting words out of her mind: "What about me, Sarah?"

Part Two:
The Hirsch Family

1. Abe Is Born

After Shifra delivered the Haberman baby she told Bertha and Yussel "Mazeltov," and left the flat. Already she felt that she was a stranger in that house as she was in this neighborhood. But she was happy, as always, after a good birth, and began the walk to Woodward Avenue and the streetcar.

It was snowing so thick that almost she couldn't see the houses across the street. She stuck out her tongue, "Like a little girl," she said and let the flakes settle on it.

One foot forward, then another, she crunched the new snow in her fine leather boots. She had gone a long block when she heard a horse and wagon behind her coming down the street. *Clop, clop.* It was a black horse pulling a black wagon loaded with coal, all wearing a white cover; the driver squinted into the storm. Shifra covered her head with her shawl. "The snow doesn't know where it falls," she said. "I could be anywhere, in my little shtetl even. A white gift from God in his heaven to carry me away. But where are the sleighs? Where are the silver and gray horses, snorting, coughing? Who is this?"

A young man had come out of a house and was waving at her. It was Morris Hirsch, husband of Reva Hirsch, who was not due for six weeks.

Mr. Hirsch was wearing his green bread delivery uniform and cap. "Don't leave, Mrs. Cohen," he shouted. "Don't go yet."

He was a little man and walked with a limp. His voice was choked; his face was twisted, like his leg. "I was coming to get you. My wife needs you now."

"Lord in his heaven," she said. "It should not be."

"Why not?" he said. "In your business anything is possible, ain't it?"

He started back to his house as fast as he could. It was hard for him to keep his balance on the snowy sidewalk. She followed and thought, *we are hurrying slowly.*

Up the stairs at last and into the flat, she went to the room at the end of the long hall. Reva Hirsch was on the bed. She had thrown off her sheet. Her nightgown was around her neck. With one hand over the other, she was holding herself between her legs.

"Nisht, nisht," Shifra said and pulled her hands away. "Mein Gott." The baby's head already showed. She took the scissors and string from her bag. Mrs. Hirsch again held her hands as if she wanted to block the infant.

"Are you mad?" Shifra said. "Do you mean to hold back your baby?"

She yelled, "I must, I must."

"You cannot, foolish girl," Shifra said. With each contraction, the baby slid out of her. Shifra had never seen anything like it. There was no stopping that baby.

"Vey iz mir!" She rushed to help, but there was nothing to do other than to catch the infant and tie the cord. "Bring a pan of warm water and a clean cloth," Shifra called out. She thought the father was in the hall outside of the bedroom.

Mrs. Hirsch was white like the pillow under her head, "My baby," she said. "How is my baby?"

"He's a fine boy," Shifra told her. "Where is the father?" He had not come back. "Doesn't he want to know? I must clean the child."

The infant was crying. Shifra put him into the cradle that was waiting next to the bed and ran to the kitchen for water and a towel. The father was nowhere to be seen. *Meshuga*, she thought.

In the bedroom, she cleaned and wrapped the baby and handed him to his mother and said, "He has fine lungs."

"Listen to him." His mother was proud of her baby's cries. "It is music. A beautiful song."

"Now you want him," Shifra said. "How could you not? He is very active. You must have got the days wrong. What will you name him?"

"Abraham." She could not stop smiling at her baby's cries. "A shtarke," she said.

"A big baby," Shifra agreed.

The infant grasped a lock of his mother's long black hair. She kissed his tiny fist. "Can I feed him?"

"Why not?" Shifra said. "If you are able. Otherwise we will give him sugar water."

"I am ready."

Shifra couldn't believe it. "You are ready. Your baby is ready. Where is the father?"

Mrs. Hirsch wasn't listening. She brought the baby to her breast. He started right away to suck.

This was how Abe Hirsch was born in the year 1915.

2. Another Baby

After Abe was born, he turned red and cried all the time. Reva stroked his tiny back and stomach. He was rigid with tension. She held him against her breasts. He sucked, but too fast. Nothing calmed him.

Can a baby be peaceful if the mother is not? God knew that Reva's heart was not easy. But she had to carry on. What else could she do? Morris would not look at Abe. He acted as if the baby was not there. Every morning at four thirty, as always, he put on his green uniform to go to his bread route. He drank leftover cold coffee and ate a day-old roll and butter. In the afternoon, he came home for his dinner. By eight o'clock he was in bed. But Abe was colicky. He screamed all night. Morris couldn't stand it. "Reva," he shouted, "stop his crying. I have to get up at four."

She held Abe, "Please don't cry. Please. Please stop crying. Let us sleep."

Finally, he did.

When Abe was two years old, Reva's sister Rae came from Chicago. She saw how Morris was with Abe but did not say anything. She had her own mishegoss, a husband who was not devoted, three children who were wild Indians. But over cigarettes and coffee, they had such laughs about the old days. For a change, Reva took her eyes off Abe. He wanted attention and poked a hairpin into an electric socket and burnt his fingers. She had to run down the street with him screaming in her arms all the way to the hospital.

When Rae went back to her family in Chicago, Reva wished that she were going with her. She began to sleep late and stayed in bed. Abe stood there and watched her. He did not take his eyes off Reva who told him to go and play, but always he came back to her bed.

She stopped making dinner for Morris and did not clean the house. She smoked all the time. She lost weight. Finally, Goody Goodman came up to talk. The Goodmans were their downstairs neighbors, and he was also their doctor. "Connie says you're thin as a rail, Reva."

"I have no appetite," Reva said.

"What does Morris say?"

"What does Morris ever say? Nothing. Zilch."

Goody looked upset. She thanked him and said that she would be okay. He said, "Reva, it's not unusual for a woman to become depressed after her first baby. The cure is to get pregnant again. It will bring your family together. It will give you a new lease on life."

Reva thought, *What an idea. Another baby. Not in this lifetime, thank you very much.*

So then, how could she explain Estelle? She didn't think it could happen again, but it did. When Goody congratulated her, she was so upset.

When Estelle was born, Morris wouldn't go near the baby. Abe stood by her crib. When she cried, he came to get Reva who told him, "You're a good brother. You're going to take care of your sister."

Abe understood. This was a lifetime instruction. He was bound to Estelle.

3. The Silence

Morris and Reva seldom spoke to each other and then in low mutters and in Yiddish, which Abe and Estelle did not understand. To them, they spoke only about the running of the home: "Abe, go to the store . . . Take out the garbage

. . . Estelle, clean your room . . . Stop that racket . . . Why don't you act good like your sister . . . ?"

The kids knew they were poor, much poorer than the Goodmans. Eddie and Albert got toys for their birthdays and for the holidays. Abe and Estelle got clothes that they knew belonged to their cousins even though the presents were given in a box with a ribbon. On weekdays, the kids were given a penny each to take to school. Ma said, "No, you can't have more. It's enough to buy a piece of candy, isn't it?"

In the mornings, before they woke up, Pa was gone to his route. Abe and Estelle knew that he took the streetcar down Woodward to the bakery where he got his wagon and his horse, Ranger. With his accent, he called him "Renger." "Whoa, Renger. Giddyup, Renger." They knew he talked funny. They thought maybe that was why he didn't talk to them.

Reva gave Morris dinner when he came home in the afternoon. When Abe and Estelle had dinner, Morris was in the living room listening to the radio or reading the *Forverts*.

Ma didn't eat with the kids either. When did she eat? They never knew.

The family didn't eat together during the week, even on Friday nights when the other families on the block used to light Shabbos candles. Family meals were on Saturday at six and Sunday at noon. Ma passed roast chicken or brisket and mashed potatoes and canned peas that Abe hated. Pa chewed and stared at the walls. They never talked to the kids. "What's new? How are things in school?" Never.

If Abe and Estelle said something, the words would float over the table like dark bubbles that took a long time to pop.

Once, after dinner, Abe ran outside to play. He yelled into the wind, "Speak, Father! Speak, Mother!"

They knew what to expect from Morris: food and a bed. But they didn't understand their mother. After Morris went to sleep, she cleaned up and, sometimes at night, talked to her neighbors. The kids listened to them tell stories and laugh. But at home, in the living room, she mended clothes until she fell asleep in her chair.

Pa was little. The picture in the kids' mind is of him in his green uniform and cap, except on weekends in the summer. Then he wore brown pants and brown suspenders and a white undershirt and played pinochle with friends from the old country. He and his friends yelled at each other during the pinochle games. Abe and Estelle used to listen and think, "He talks to them."

In their room on their cots, Estelle cried.

"He hates me."

"He doesn't hate you. He's just mad about something."

"She doesn't care about me. Why doesn't she want to know anything about me? Other kids' mothers care about them."

"Listen. You've got me. I care about you. I'll tell you what to do."

"Can I come in your bed?"

"Only for a little while. What are you doing? Stop that, Estelle."

"My legs are snakes, Abe. I'm winding you."

"Stop it. I don't like to be wound."

"Abe?"

"What?"

"Where does a man put his whizzer into a girl?"

"What do you mean, for God's sake? Why do you want to know?"

"Are you mad at me, Abe?"

"You better not be doing any of that stuff, Estelle."

"I'm not doing anything. Why don't you answer me? Maybe you don't know either."

"That's dumb. Go back to your bed."

"Abe?"

"What?"

"Do you know where men put it?"

"Yes."

"Have you done it?"

"No."

"Good night."

4. Nutty Moie

The Hirsch family lived in a second-floor flat of a two-family brick house. All the houses had a small lawn in front, barely big enough to hold a gnarly plane tree. An unattached garage in back was reached by a side drive. Morris never owned a car, but later on, he parked his bread truck in the garage.

Estelle was younger and smaller than the other kids. She was allowed to play because Abe said so. She stayed close to him during the rubber gun wars, but she could roam like the others during games of tag and especially hide-and-go-seek when they looked for hiding places, there were lots of them, behind garage doors, inside falling-down sheds, behind half-dismantled wooden fences or in thrown-away iceboxes. So when Estelle didn't show up after everyone else had touched home or been tagged out, none of them was worried.

"She's smart," Abe told them. "She can hide anywhere."

"Estelle," they began to yell. "Estelle, . . . come in. The game is over."

The kids began to ask what they should play next. This started an argument between kids who wanted to play tag and others who wanted a rubber gun war.

Abe said, "We better find Estelle."

Eddie and Albert, who did not want her around anyway, said, "She went into her house. Let's play. Come on, let's play, Abe."

Abe knew that Estelle hated their house. He said, "Who saw where she went?"

Henny, a red-headed kid who lived in the last house toward Twelfth Street, said, "I saw her. She went up Wolfman's drive."

"Let's see," Abe said. They all ran to the drive. They yelled, "Estelle! Where are you? The game's over. Come out!"

Estelle did not appear.

"All right," Abe said, "I want to find her."

Eddie said, "Maybe something happened to Estelle."

"Maybe she's in trouble," Albert said.

Henny said, "What should we do, Abe?"

He thought for a moment and told them that everyone would take a different side drive. They would check the whole block and meet out front.

They yelled, "Estelle! Estelle!" and ran up and down the drives. Estelle was still missing.

The gang gathered again. Abe told them that they had to find her.

Eddie said, "Maybe Estelle was kidnapped."

"This is Kirby Street, dummy," Albert told his brother. "There are no kidnappers on Kirby Street."

Abe held up his hand to quiet them. "Did anybody see anything, anything funny?"

The kids looked at one another. They saw that he was upset.

"A-a-a-b-e." It was Izzy, who almost never spoke. Izzy stuttered, and kids laughed at him.

"What?" Abe stepped toward him.

"Oh, oh," Eddie said.

Izzy stepped back.

Abe asked Izzy what he had seen.

Izzy shook his head.

Abe promised him that nobody would laugh.

Izzy stared at the ground.

Abe asked him again if he had seen somebody.

Izzy shook his head yes.

"Who," Abe yelled. "Who was it, Izzy?"

Izzy tried. "Nnnnnnn . . ."

"Come on, Izzy," Albert yelled.

"Nnnnnnnn . . ."

Henny used to play alone with Izzy at times, and once in a while he could figure out what he wanted to say. "Izzy, was it Nutty Moie?"

Izzy nodded and looked happy.

They all knew Nutty Moie. They saw him a lot in the neighborhood. He wore torn black pants. They could see his skin through the holes and were pretty sure that he didn't wear underwear. His jacket was tied with a filthy piece of rope. His hat was a beanie, and he pinned on different buttons like the Communists, the Zionists and the Socialists. His old boots were untied; they could see that his feet were dirty. He wandered around talking to himself, sometimes shouting at invisible people. Sometimes the kids ran close to get a whiff of his terrible body smell, swerving at the last minute. They thought that Moie was harmless, but kept their distance unless they felt safe because there were a lot of them.

Abe knew that Estelle wouldn't think about danger and that she could talk to Nutty Moie like he was somebody else's father. So he yelled, "Where did you see him? Where, Izzy?"

Izzy pointed to the Wolfman's side drive.

"Come on," Abe shouted and led the gang back up the drive.

He tried the side door. It was unlocked. He stepped inside. He called out, "Estelle ..."

There was no answer. "Wait here," he told the gang who stayed outside the door.

The basement was dark. Abe felt for the light switch, but couldn't find it.

"Estelle ..."

He crept down the stairs and could make out the basement walls by the dim light that came through the dirty windows. He heard a rustle from behind the door to the coal bin. His heart was pounding. He slowly opened the door and could tell that somebody was standing next to the coal pile.

"Moie," Abe said, "if that's you, you should get out of here. Now. We won't stop you."

A man groaned, rushed toward him and knocked him down, then ran up the cellar stairs and out to the driveway. Abe could hear the shouts of his gang. He got up and stepped toward the coal pile. "Estelle?"

"Abe?" Her voice was thin, like a whisper.

He yelled, "Oh, God!" and fell on the pile. He pulled at the pieces of coal and found Estelle totally buried.

He pushed the coal off her and pulled her to her feet. She was shaking and said, "Abe, I'm sorry. Abe, I'm sorry."

He led her up the cellar steps. The kids, who were scattered up and down the drive from the shock of Nutty Moie running out of the basement among them, were shocked all over again. "Hey hey," they yelled. "It's Estelle ... Look at

Estelle . . . Moie got Estelle . . . Estelle, are you okay? Are you okay?"

She was black with coal dust from head to toe, but she surprised them with an odd sort of smile. Not a "ha ha" smile, but a "look what I did" smile. She told them in a whispering voice, "We were playing a game. It was fun. For a while."

None of the gang knew what to say. They stared at her, a black ghost.

Abe looked at her, his dark sister. "Wait'll Mom sees you."

Estelle smiled her funny smile again.

He took her hand and led her home. When they reached their house, she started to cry and could not stop until he ran the water in the bathtub. She was still in the tub when Reva came home. Abe told her what had happened, and she sat down hard. Morris, when he heard the story, cursed at Estelle then said nothing more about it.

Later, in their room, Estelle said, "He didn't have to curse at me."

By this time, Abe was shaking. He said, "He was right. If it wasn't so scary, I would have cursed at you. Why did you go with Nutty Moie?"

"He seemed nice," Estelle said. "He said we could play a game."

"He better not come back to this neighborhood," Abe told her.

"I wasn't worried. I knew you would save me."

"I was almost too late."

"I know," Estelle said and started to cry again. She cried on and off all night.

5. Be a Man

Reva was taller than Morris. He never stood next to her. When Abe was a teenager, he never stood next to Morris because by then he was six feet tall, and his shoulders were way bigger than his father's. Abe and Estelle never talked about Morris' limp. He never told them what happened to his leg. Maybe he was born with it, they thought. Maybe that made him meaner.

Reva was dreamy. She used to sit front of her mirror and wind her long black hair into a bun. She daydreamed in the middle of her housework and liked the soap operas on the radio. She talked about them with her friends, mostly in Yiddish, but the kids knew. In Yiddish, Stella Dallas is Stella Dallas. Mary Worth is Mary Worth.

Ma used to touch them. She tucked in Abe's shirt when he went to school. She combed Estelle's hair. *She kisses us,* Abe thought. *Why doesn't she ask us things?*

Around the house, Reva wore a housecoat. But when she went out for groceries or just for walking and looking in store windows, she dressed up with lipstick and rouge. When Abe was ten, he saw that men used to look at his mother, and she would pretend not to notice. But he saw her face. She liked it. He didn't like it. Ma smiled a lot, especially with the butchers at Grossman's, and they would give her extra meat.

On hot nights, Ma and Pa left the bedroom doors open. The kids' room was across from theirs. When Abe was sure that Estelle was sleeping, he would watch his ma undress. She was slow to undress. Sometimes she would stand still before she took off her brassiere, then stand still again before she put on her nightgown, sometimes with her back to him, sometimes sideways, and he could see her breasts. Sometimes she looked towards the kids' room. Abe would shut his eyes. He thought in the dark how could she know that his eyes were barely open? Did she know? Did she guess? He couldn't stand to think so.

One night, it had to be a Saturday because Pa was still up, Morris and Reva argued. It started in the living room. They spit out hissing words, getting louder and louder as they moved down the hall. Abe looked to see if Estelle was awake. He couldn't tell. Outside of their bedroom he could have understood them, but didn't want to and put the pillow over his head. He heard his ma. "Shah! Shah!" And their bedroom door closed. He heard Pa's voice. "What do you think I am? Of stone I'm not made." There was more hissing. Finally, he fell asleep.

At breakfast, as usual, silence. Ma wasn't looking at them. She put cereal and milk on the table and went back into her bedroom. Abe looked at Estelle. She was sitting on the edge of her chair. The skin on her face was tight. She had heard everything last night. She ate a little cereal and stood up. "I hate it here," she said and went to their room for her book bag. "I'm going." She didn't wait for him.

Ma came out of her room. "Where's Estelle?"

He didn't answer. He just stared at her.

She was a million miles away. She turned her back to Abe, opened her dressing gown and, for a long time, looked at her body. Stilll facing away from him, she said, "Abe, you're a smart boychick, and I'm going to tell you something important. Whatever you do when you grow up and get married, be a man." She closed her gown, walked back to her bedroom and shut the door.

He knew she was telling him that Pa was not a man. And that's what they were arguing about last night. But how was Pa not a man? In what way? He didn't know. But he knew that he would have to figure it out before he got married.

6. Estelle

When Estelle was small, Abe protected her from boys who teased and tripped her and tried to pull her hair. This was a job because she used to dare all of them and tell him to beat them up. When she was twelve, Abe warned her about boys who were dangerous. She was so pretty and had that little smile, and she had a hard time staying away from them.

At night, he told her, "If you go with Billy again, I'll bust his head and yours, too, dummy."

"I'll stay away from him, Abe."

"You better."

"He's so good-looking."

"Never mind."

"You'll be my boyfriend, Abe."

"Go to sleep."

"Good night, boyfriend."

"Shut up."

"Abe?"

"What?"

"Remember when you used to let me come into your bed?"

"Yeah. So what?"

"I wish I was little again . . . Abe?"

"What? You're not little anymore. And I'm not either."

"I know."

"Good night."

"Good night, boyfriend."

7. Home Care

The Hirsch's lived in the second-floor flat of a two-story house. Their living room overlooked the street and also opened into the dining room with its heavy oak table and dark oak chairs with brown and yellow upholstered seats. In the kitchen, across the hall from the dining room, was a big porcelain coal-burning stove and a maple table whose top was marred with rings left by glasses and coffee cups, also four folding chairs that had been bought at the Workman's Circle thrift shop. Down the hall were a bathroom with a shower bathtub and three bedrooms. Morris and Reva used one rear bedroom; Abe and Estelle shared the other. A third smaller bedroom for visiting family was across from the bathroom.

Morris made enough money on his bread route to pay the rent, $35.00 a month, and usually enough for food; Reva hated to ask for credit, but did it when she had to. Also, in the winter they had to buy coal at $4.50 a month.

When Abe or Estelle was sick, Goody Goodman came up. He showed Reva how to set up a camphor oil steam tent, especially when Estelle had the croup.

When Abe was four, he fussed about a tooth that wouldn't fall out. Morris tied a long string to the tooth and fastened the other end to a doorknob of an open door. "All right," he said, "open your mouth." Abe did. Morris slammed the door shut. The tooth shot across the room and clanged into a vase on the dining room table. Pa smiled. Abe felt the space where his tooth was with his tongue. Morris said, "From now on, I don't want to hear about your teeth."

When Abe was ten, he got a fever. Reva finally had to call up Goody Goodman. He told her that Abe had scarlet fever and had to stay in bed for three weeks and could not even walk to the bathroom. The next day, a public health officer tacked a quarantine sign to the door of the house. Reva took care of Abe. She fed him cherry Jell-O, rice and milk, and lots of water. Morris and Estelle had to go downstairs to live with the Goodmans.

At first, Abe slept a lot, but there were times when Reva played cards with him, Casino and Go Fish, and once she even set up a jigsaw puzzle on the table next to his bed. He never forgot the feeling of closeness and of being taken care of.

One night she turned on the radio in the living room loud enough so that he could hear a rabbi offering a prayer. It was in Hebrew. Reva told Abe that the prayer was for him, that she had paid for it, and that the Radio Rabbi was famous for reaching God.

Another time, he heard his name being called from the outside. From the end of his bed, he looked down through the window and saw Estelle and the two Goodman boys waving.

After three weeks, Goody said that he was recovering and should dangle his feet over the side of the bed, for two days, three times a day, before he could walk to the bathroom. He had to hold on to Reva the first time.

A week later, Morris and Estelle moved back up. "I didn't like it down there," Estelle told Abe. "Mrs. Goodman is a terrible cook. She made peas a lot. And Eddie and Albert picked on me."

8. Dan

Abe always wanted to make money. When he was nine, he delivered the *Detroit News* on foot. Morris wouldn't buy him a bicycle. In the winter, he got home after dark.

When he was fifteen, he got a job as soda jerk in Dan's pharmacy; he worked from 4:00 a.m. to 6:30 p.m. on weekdays and all day on Saturday making ice cream sodas, sundaes, milk shakes, malteds and banana splits. Dan's was closed on Sundays.

The kids from school tried to get Abe to give them extra large dips of ice cream and free refills on Cokes. He wouldn't, even for Estelle.

She said, "I told my friends you would do it for me."

He said, "I'll lose my job. Dan trusts me."

Dan was a big man, tall, heavy and bald. He looked worried all the time. He said that his customers brought him their prescriptions because they depended on him to mix the medications accurately and not overcharge them. "They come because they trust me," he said. "And you can have this job because I think I can trust you. The last kid was giving free stuff to his friends, and I've seen the girls looking at you. Can I trust you?"

"Yes, sir." And he meant it.

"No free Cokes or extra dips, even to my wife."

"Even to your wife?" Abe thought that was a little funny.

"That's right."

"What if she won't pay?"

Dan laughed. "Of course she won't pay. But you'll tell me, and I'll put the money in the register. Okay? There's a white jacket and cap in the storage room."

Dan paid thirty-five cents an hour. Each week, Pa made Abe give everything over a dollar to Ma, and he put at least twenty-five cents into the shoebox under his bed. He was saving for high-top leather boots. The boots cost twelve dollars.

He liked the job. He could take care of a whole counter of customers. After a few weeks, Dan stopped watching him. After work, Dan and Abe used to make sundaes for themselves, the crazier the better: chocolate and strawberry ice cream with pineapple topping covered with nuts and whipped cream; orange ice with hot caramel fudge, banana slices and maraschino cherries; hazelnut ice cream with every sauce at the counter-chocolate, caramel, strawberry, pineapple, blueberry, cherry and peach; and a tower of whipped cream and pistachio nuts.

Best of all? Even though he was always tired and sat down at the counter and didn't want to move, Dan talked to Abe.

"So, kid, what're ya gonna be when you grow up?"

What a question, Abe thought. "Dunno."

"Get an education, kid. You could be a pharmacist. Even a doctor. I'd help you."

Fat chance. "I don't know. I gotta work. I got no money to go to college."

"Horse feathers." Dan didn't like for Abe to contradict him. "I didn't have it easy. I worked my way through college. What d'ya think? I had it easy?"

Abe told him what he wanted to hear. "I'll try. I'm not great in school."

He patted Abe's shoulder. "You're gonna do it. And I'll be here to make sure you do it. Okay? Is it a deal?"

"Sure." *Why not?*

He told Estelle about it. She said, "He likes you. He really talks to you."

"Yeah."

Both of them sat on their beds and thought about a grown man really talking to a kid.

Estelle said, "Doesn't he have kids of his own?"

"I guess not. He never said nothing about kids and none ever come to the store, only his wife, once in a while."

"Maybe he'll help you, Abe."

"Soap bubbles." He couldn't believe that, but couldn't get the thought out of his mind either. And Dan kept after Abe.

After sundaes, he said, "When do you study?"

"At night after dinner."

"Your parents make you study?"

That was a good one. "They don't need to. I study."

"Since when?" He had a face he made when Abe said something he didn't believe, like if he had to swallow something that tasted bad.

Closing up the store, Dan asked who looked at Abe's homework. Abe didn't answer. He just walked away.

The next day, Dan apologized, "I'm butting into your business."

Abe didn't want Dan to drop him. "It's okay."

"I want to help. You're such a serious kid. You never laugh, and I thought you must be a studier. Now I don't think so, and I want to know what's going on with your schoolwork."

Abe yelled at him. "I take care of myself!"

Dan yelled right back. "You can't take care of yourself. You're a kid. You need help. All kids need help."

"Not me." Abe walked to the sink and began to wash glasses and stack them on a rack.

Dan followed him. "What subject do you have the most trouble in?"

"Arithmetic." Abe had to answer him.

"Good," Dan said. "Now we're getting somewhere. From now on, after work, we spend a half an hour working on arithmetic."

Estelle couldn't believe it. "He really likes you."

"He wants to know about you, too," Abe told her. "He wants you to come by the store."

"He must not have kids of his own."

The arithmetic lessons expanded to grammar and handwriting. "You're a smart kid," Dan said. "Who do you take after?"

"Nobody."

Dan was eating his sundae. He worked his spoon around until he had a small mountain of ice cream and sauce balanced on it. He looked at the spoon and said, "You must take after somebody. Is your father tall?"

Abe laughed. "Not him."

"What about your mother? Is she pretty?"

Abe just looked at him.

Dan said, "Too bad you can't go out for sports," and put the whole spoonful into his mouth.

Abe told Estelle, "He thinks I should be a sports star."

She said, "You're a fast runner."

He said, "I have to be to keep you out of trouble."

When Estelle came to the store to meet Dan, he stared at her until she started to squirm. "I thought it was you," he said. "I've seen you here before. You probably do your homework, right? Not like your big shot brother." Estelle giggled and poked Abe in the ribs.

"Cut that out," he told her.

Dan smiled at her. "You're a pretty girl." Then he surprised Abe. "Give her a sundae. Free. Just this once." And he walked to the back of the store to work on prescriptions.

Abe poked her like she poked him. "He likes you too."

She just stood there smiling, then sat at the counter.

Summer. Abe worked full-time. Estelle ran around all day; nobody watched her. Once she came home with a black eye. Reva screamed and ran to Grossman's for a piece of beef.

Morris was home. He looked at Estelle and said, "Feh."

When Abe got home, Estelle told him that Timothy Ryan had punched her in the eye and that she had given him a bloody nose. Abe told her she had to stay away from those Irish kids. She told him she was okay and wouldn't do anything bad. He told Dan about it. He told Abe to bring her to the store, and he would lay down the law. So she came and stood there in front of him, swaying from one foot to the other and that flirty smile on her face. He was soft with her. He said, "You got to be careful, honey."

She promised she would. He told her to come to the store in the afternoons so he could see that she was okay and not playing in a bad neighborhood. And he would let her have a free Coke. So of course, she did. She would wait in front of the store until Abe waved her in. Dan would give her the once-over and go back to his pills.

That fall, before Rosh Hashanah, Abe came to work and the store was closed, locked. No Dan. Abe came three days in a row. No one. But on the fourth day, a stranger was walking around inside the store. He was carrying a notebook and writing things down. He was a tall man, skinny and bald. He had a long mustache that hung down, and he was dressed in black pants and jacket, a gray shirt and a black string tie. He had a sad look on his face. When Abe told him who he was, the man said that he was Irving, Dan's wife's brother, and that Dan had died of a stroke.

Irving was listing everything in the store. He told Abe that Dan's wife was putting it up for sale. "My sister needs the money to live on. Dan didn't hardly have no insurance."

Abe just stared at him. *What? What? What are you saying?* He was numb.

Irving looked like he felt sorry for Abe who asked him what insurance was.

"What's the difference?" Irving said. "It don't matter if you don't have any. You want to help list things? We'll pay your regular wage."

Abe didn't want to, but he did. When they finished, he felt so bad. He felt like it couldn't be true. He didn't want to leave the store. but there was nothing more to do. Irving asked if Abe wanted an ice cream. Abe shook his head. He couldn't eat that ice cream.

9. Butcher Boy

The next few weeks, Abe couldn't stop looking for Dan. He kept going past the store. It was always closed with the lights off. He couldn't do his homework because Dan wasn't helping him. He didn't want another job, but needed the money. So he went from store to store on Twelfth Street: Pearlman, who sold notions, thread, needles, measuring tapes, that sort of stuff; Ginsberg's hardware, he liked being in his place, he liked the tools; Frenchy, who had the little delicatessen (he wasn't French, but he wore a beret); Herman's Bakery, he didn't really want that job, he would have had to get up at three in the morning. He knew most of the storeowners, but nobody needed help. Finally, Abe got a job with Meyer Grossman, the butcher. He was surprised when Meyer hired him on the spot. Then it turned out Meyer had been a friend of Dan's. "Dan told me about you. I can use a big kid who's a hard worker to help around the shop. I don't suppose you know anything about the butcher business?"

Abe told him he didn't.

"That's okay," Meyer said. "The pay is thirty-five cents an hour, plus tips. Help yourself to a pickle."

He pointed to a pickle barrel set in the back corner of the shop. Customers helped themselves all day long. Abe didn't know that he would be watching customers fish for pickles for more than fifty years until he sold the store and retired.

The only thing Abe knew about Mr. Grossman was that he heard someone tell his mom that you had to watch his thumb on the scale. After he worked there for a week, he could see that once in a while he helped the scale, not a lot, just enough to make a few extra pennies.

The other thing about Meyer Grossman, according to Abe's mother and her friends, was that Meyer looked like one of his pickles, which was a funny thing to say, but Abe could see what they meant. Meyer was wide in the middle, like a fat pickle, with his stomach pushing out his white apron. He had a small head and small feet. And his skin was gray, almost greenish in the store lights. He walked funny; bouncing like his shoes always hurt. He had a shiny, bald head and always had a cigar stub in his mouth. Sometimes his cigar ashes would fall on a piece of meat. He would laugh and rub it in and say, "Smoked flanken. A delicacy. We'll raise the price."

After Abe took a pickle, Meyer told him that they closed on Friday before sundown and opened Sunday morning from nine until noon. Otherwise, during the week they closed by six or six thirty, depending on the customers.

Abe asked Meyer what the tips were for.

"When you do deliveries," Meyer said, "on our bicycle." Then he yelled to a young guy behind the counter, "Joey, when you're done with Mrs. Bloom . . . Hello, Mrs. Bloom, darling." A little old lady in black, somebody's bubbe who didn't like to be interrupted, looked at Mr. Grossman and went back to talking with Joey. Joey held up his hand to tell her to wait a minute while Mr. Grossman told him, "When you're finished with Mrs. Bloom—I'm not hurrying you, Mrs. Bloom—I say, Joey, when you're finished with Mrs. Bloom to her satisfaction, I say . . ." He smiled at her and bowed; she looked irritated. "Then, Joey, take Abe here who is our new assistant into the back room and show him how to clean up before 'you know who' comes. Okay?"

Joey waved okay to Mr. Grossman, waved hello to Abe and went back to waiting on Mrs. Bloom.

Abe walked to the back of the store and watched them. Mrs. Bloom was giving Joey a lot of instructions and waving her finger at him. She wanted to make sure that he knew exactly what she was ordering, a piece of lamb cut in a certain way, nothing else would do. Joey was a big, good-looking guy with a lot of black hair parted on the left side; he had a friendly smile and looked strong enough to lift a cow's carcass by himself. He was much younger than Mr. Grossman and the other butcher, Seymour.

Joey smiled at Mrs. Bloom and nodded. But his eyes kept looking away. Abe had the feeling that he really wasn't listening to her, and she must have had the same feeling because she was getting loud and suddenly she walked around the end of the counter and grabbed hold of his white apron and kept pulling on it until he said, "Mrs. Bloom, you know what?" and he repeated exactly what she had been telling him. Then he winked at her, and she yelled at him in Yiddish. He laughed and lifted her up by her waist and carried her to the customers' side of the counter. She looked totally happy.

Seymour, the other butcher, was a short guy with a long face, a big nose and a black beard that made him look like an Orthodox Jew, except he wore a white butcher's cap instead of a yarmulke. Also, he wore spectacles. He seemed like a serious person that you could trust. But when he walked past Abe, he said in a low voice, "You know the most important thing about the butcher business, kid? Keep the customers happy. Kibitz with them. Shtup them. You'll see." And he poked Abe in the ribs and giggled like a girl. What a place this was! Nothing like Dan's, that's for sure. Abe decided that butchers must be a little meshuga. He knew he was going to like it.

Joey waved him through the door into the back room. "Okay, kiddo, let's get to work. We got to clean this place up before Rabbi Fingerhut comes to inspect."

So that's who was coming. A big shot rabbi. Abe knew the rabbis came to inspect to make sure that the shop was clean and that the meat was strictly kosher and had the *plumba*, the kosher seal of his religious group.

The back room was cool. Big blocks of ice covered with sawdust were kept in bins along the two sidewalls. In the middle of the room were two big butcher-block tables covered with bloody parts of meat. On the wood floor, scraps of meat and blood were mixed in with sawdust. Whole sides of beef and lamb and a couple dozen chickens and ducks were hung on hooks screwed into the tin ceiling. There were two cabinets attached to a wall and a closet in the back. There were six cane chairs, three on each side of the closet. There were two big trash cans with bent lids. There was a big metal sink with two long faucets for hot and cold. The brooms, the mops, the dustpan, the cleaning materials, the rags were in the closet and one of the cabinets.

"We keep our medical supplies in the other cabinet," Joey said. "Look." He opened the cabinet and took out a big dark bottle labeled with a red skull and crossbones and the word *iodine*. He opened the bottle and sniffed. He looked at Abe and rolled his eyes like he was a little crazy. Abe thought, *What is he doing?* Joey took a big swallow, smacked his lips and said, "Great stuff." He screwed on the cap and put back the bottle. Later, when they were cleaning, Abe got close to him and smelled the schnapps .

Joey pushed all the meat scraps off the tables onto the floor. They scrubbed down the tables with stiff brushes and a mixture of hot water, kosher salt and ammonia. After that, they swept the floor, dumping the sawdust into the garbage cans. Finally, they mopped the floor with ammonia in hot water. The place looked and smelled clean. They were ready for the rabbi who came in with Mr. Grossman while Joey and Abe were admiring their work.

Rabbi Fingerhut was a little old guy from the old country with a long white beard, a long black coat and a wide-brimmed black hat, the regular outfit of the Orthodox that they saw around the neighborhood. He poked around the room, sniffing and looking and talking to himself, or to the Lord, in a singsong voice, "Nu, nu? Vous mahkst du Yid? How are the Jews?" When he finished, he smiled at Mr. Grossman and said, "Nu?"

Meyer smiled. He danced over to the medicine cabinet and pulled out the iodine bottle. He took off the cap, looked inside and shook his head at Joey, who laughed. Mr. Grossman smiled again and brought the bottle to the rabbi who said a blessing, took a big drink, then called out, "Danka, danka schein. Thanks very much." And he left.

This happened before Abe had been working at Grossman's for less than an hour.

His job after school was to clean the back room by himself; also after the shop closed, to wipe down the counters, clean the glass cases and sweep and mop the whole place. The best was the deliveries. He liked to look at people's kitchens.

He told Estelle, "You get a feeling about people from their kitchens. Sometimes the family is home."

She said, "So what? Who cares?"

"What d'ya mean?"

"So if somebody delivers meat to our flat?" She was sarcastic. "And they see our kitchen?"

"Yeah?"

"And they can see what things are like here?"

"You don't get it," he said. "Some places are nice. Sometimes mothers laugh a lot. Sometimes they kid around. It's friendly. I like it."

Estelle was serious. "What good does it do, Abe?"

"I see how I want to live someday."

She gave him a little smile. "Maybe there are girls."

"Only mothers," he told her. "Old mothers."

10. Tillie

None of her crowd could understand why she married Eli. Tillie could have told them that she was a grown-up, and being grown-up is when you swallow your kid dreams and do the smart thing. And you don't complain. You accept the bargain you made. You keep your head up and live with it.

"You're Tillie," they said. "You could have had anybody."

Any slob, they meant.

"Eli Goldsmith, of all people, Tillie. Why?"

Why? Because this was a hard place to grow up. Everyone struggled. My father liked books. The kind you read. Books don't put food on the table. Eli Goldsmith's father started Goldsmith's Jewelers. Eli is rich. Who cares if he's a funny-looking little guy? Who cares if he . . .

". . . chews with his mouth open, Tillie."

". . . chews with his mouth open. So big fat what, sister!"

She made her bed, as the saying goes. So what if Eli grunts a lot and finishes in two minutes. None of her crowd will hear anything about that. Anyway, what's sex? Tillie knew she wasn't marrying Mr. Rudy Valley.

So what? She knew she could go to Hudson's and buy anything she wanted. She could spend the summer in South Haven and go to Miami Beach in March. No questions from Eli. He was glad to have her. As long as he thought she was staying in line. If not, he didn't want to hear about it.

So what if she had a little fun with the kid? If Lila hadn't gotten sick, she and Abe never would have met. She never would have laid eyes on him. Gorgeous Abe.

What happened? Lila was out with a cold. Tillie was getting dressed to go downtown, and the back doorbell rang. She put on her dressing gown, lit a cigarette and pushed the buzzer. Into the kitchen walked this young Jewish god carrying a package of meat.

"Delivery from Grossman's, ma'am."

Delivery from Grossman's! Special delivery from Grossman's. Gorgeous body. Gorgeous face. Gorgeous brown eyes. Innocent? Don't ask. Special delivery to Tillie.

Just a minute, she told him and went to her room for her purse. She came back. They talked a little. He told her his name was Abe. He told her the bill was three seventy-five. She pulled the belt tight on her dressing gown so that he could see her breasts better.

He was trying to stay calm, but his eyes were getting big. So was something else. He couldn't help himself. She asked if he liked working for Grossman. She looked like her mind was elsewhere and scratched under her left breast. He was turning pink and backed up to the door. She told him that Grossman was stingy and not to let him take advantage. She handed him four dollars. He swallowed and gave her back a quarter.

"Butchers are strong men, aren't they, Abe?" she said in her little girl voice. She gave him a nickel tip and held his hand for just a second.

"For you, Abe," she told him. He looked like he was glad to escape. She laughed. What a prize. He didn't know what was waiting for him.

Next week, when the doorbell rang, Lila answered it. Tillie heard them in the kitchen. She wandered in and said, "Oh, hello there. You're the young man from Grossman's." Lila gave her a look. Tillie smiled and said, "Lila, have you seen my pearl earrings? I can't find them." And she smiled at Abe, as if they were sharing a joke.

He didn't know what to make of it. Lila did. Tillie explained to Abe, "I'm terrible at misplacing things."

Lila didn't like the whole thing. She said, "I'll see as I can find them." She walked out of the kitchen.

Tillie said, "Well, Abe, how have you been?"

He said, "Ma'am?" and looked at the floor.

"Is something the matter, Abe?" she said.

He looked up at her, right in the eyes, bold as anything. Now she felt her heart skip. She couldn't believe a kid would affect her like that. She just looked at him. Lila came back with the earrings. "Where you always keeps them," she said.

Tillie smiled at her and at Abe. She told Lila to tip him ten cents and left the room. She leaned on the kitchen door, a little out of breath. She heard them talking.

Lila told Abe to get someone else to deliver the meat.

"Why?" he said. "I ain't doing nothing wrong."

"Not yet you ain't," she said. She sounded angry. "Better watch your step, butcher boy. We both gonna lose our jobs."

"Why's that?" he said.

She said, "Because you foolin' with a customer, and I in the way."

She was right about half of it, anyway.

11. No, Abe

Boys played with themselves in the bathroom. Estelle did it in bed and had to hold still and not make a sound because Abe was there behind the curtain. So when she walked into the bathroom, and he was standing in front of the toilet, and she saw him get red and hurry to button his fly, she said, "Excuse me." Then she laughed and said, "What are you doing?"

And he said, "Estelle, don't you know about privacy in the bathroom?"

And she said, "Sorry, sorry, I didn't know you were home." Then she said, she couldn't resist it, "I didn't know you did that."

"It's none of your business," he yelled at her.

"I do it too," she told him. She knew he couldn't stand that.

He really was sore. "Keep your sex life to yourself!" He was aggravated and walked out of the bathroom. He wouldn't look at her.

She yelled after him, "I do!" *Oh, God*, she thought, *I love this.*

So they were doing the dishes. Abe washed as usual. She dried. Ma was out somewhere. Pa was sleeping. They could hear him snore when the water wasn't running. Estelle liked doing the dishes with Abe. They talked. They sang songs a lot. It was usually a peaceful time. But now Abe was dreaming. He was somewhere else. More than that, she could tell that he was excited about something, something he wasn't talking about. She was determined to find out.

"So?"

Abe looked at her. "So what?"

"Sew buttons," she told him. He didn't want to tell her what was going on. But really, in a way, she knew that he wanted her to know. They were so used to sharing everything. She knew she would find out if she kept after him. She sang one of their songs. "Oh, Abey would waltz with a strawberry blond . . ."

Abe went back to scrubbing the frying pan. He knew what she was after and said, "Leave me alone, Estelle."

She poked him in the ribs, which he hated.

"Stop that," he yelled.

"What's her name?" she yelled. She tried to poke him again, but he blocked her and got her dress wet.

"Mary Pickford," he said. He dropped the frying pan into the dishwater and threw up a lot of soap bubbles.

He couldn't keep a secret from her. She said, "Were you thinking about someone when you were in the bathroom?"

And he said, "Well, I certainly wasn't thinking about you."

That went too far. She made an angry face. "Abe!"

He made a sorry face. "Sorry."

She was mad. "Shall I tell you who I think about when I do that?"

"Listen," he said, "let's drop this."

"Anyway," she told him, "You look like a radish. I think I'll chop you up into a salad."

That was better. He said, "We'll need onions. I'll chop up your finger."

"Maybe you know someone who's sweet. One of those mothers."

He looked her in the eyes and said right out, "Maybe I do."

She thought, *Oh, Abe. No. Don't leave me alone, Abe. I need you. Oh, Abe, please.* And so she wouldn't cry, she said, "You better bring her around so I can inspect her."

He took a deep breath. "I can't do that, silly." He had a way of talking to her that was private and confidential. Usually she loved it, but this time, with his private tone of voice, he said, "Anyway, it has nothing to do with you and me."

She thought, *Oh, no? That's what you think, mister.* She said, "Abe . . ."

"Let's sing," he said, her calm, handsome brother. "Daisy, Daisy, give me your answer true."

She sang, "I'm half crazy all for the love of you."

They both sang, "It won't be a stylish marriage. I can't afford a carriage . . ."

"Oh, Abe."

"It has nothing to do with us," he said again. "But certain things happen. And that's how it is."

"I know all about that," she told him. Abe shivered. She was thinking about a certain someone who wanted to do it. So far she had said no. But she knew she wouldn't tell Abe either way.

12. Fooling Around

Tillie wasn't the only wife who wore a dressing gown around the house. Some of them didn't care about keeping their gowns closed, as if it didn't matter around a delivery boy, or they thought he was only a kid, or they were too busy to care about how it looked. One thing, he got an education on girdles; some of them went up high like a brassiere, other ones went to the waist. Both kinds had garter clips hanging down to attach to stockings.

Two of the women didn't wear brassieres. One of them brushed against him all the time when she was looking for her purse. Once, a pretty colored maid told him to sit on a chair while she went for the money. When she came back, she sat on his lap and kissed him and told him that the money was in her bra. He put his hand on her breast and pinched her big nipple, not hard, grabbed the money, and headed for the door. She said, "Hey, dopey, where you goin'?"

One evening after closing, he was sweeping the sawdust. Little Seymour had the idea that all of the customers were waiting for Abe like spiders in their webs. "So, kid, you're looking a little tired out."

"Not me."

"Are you kidding? A good-looking kid! You're just what they're after."

Mr. Grossman didn't like that. "Seymour, don't instigate him."

"Meyer," he said. "I wouldn't instigate."

Abe got red. Joey laughed. "You're embarrassing him."

Mr. Grossman said, "Don't fool with the customers, Abe."

Joey thought it was funny. "He wouldn't, Meyer. Would you, Abe?"

Abe shook his head. He didn't want to lie out loud.

Tillie had three dressing gowns: the green one with the sash she liked to pull tight, a tan gown with big red-and-orange flowers and a gray gown with little black-and-white boxes. When she wore the green gown, she was ready for a quick one.

Her maid, Lila, was right. She was in the way, and she was gone. Tillie said, "Who cares?" when he asked where Lila was. That was the first time Tillie told him to come into her bedroom to help find her purse that was always getting lost, once in her bureau drawer under her blouses; once under the bed; once in the blanket on her bed; once, Tillie had a hunch, on a high shelf in her closet.

To find it, he had to stand on a chair. "I don't see it."

"It must be there," she said. "Don't move. I'm coming up to help you."

They were both standing on the chair, giggling. She unbuttoned his fly and held him.

"We'll never get to the bed," he said. He was right.

The first time, in bed, Tillie told him, "You were a virgin."

"I was not."

She laughed and said, "Honey, you are sweet like an orange lollypop and you have a body like Charles Atlas. But this is something I know a lot about, believe me, and something I'm going to teach you about, lucky you." She put her hand on him. "Now, once more real quick and then you have to scram out of here."

One time, after sex, he felt like they should talk a little. "So what do you think about what's happening in Russia?"

"What?" Tillie sat up. He stared at her breasts and forgot about Russia. But she said, "What do you mean, 'Russia?'"

He felt himself blush. "The pogroms . . . I just wondered."

She reached for a cigarette. "You make love to me and you think about the pogroms?"

Now he was uncomfortable. "No. It's not that way. It's just that this is all we do."

"So what's the matter with that?"

"Nothing. Of course. But I thought, well . . ."

"Don't think," she said. She blew a cloud of smoke out of the side of her mouth. "Thinking is the enemy of sex. And sex is why you're here."

Three months after they started, she opened the door and was wearing her flowered dressing gown. She took the meat and handed him a flat box wrapped in nice paper and tied with a red ribbon. "Open it."

It was a black leather wallet. "It's not my birthday."

"It's a thank-you gift. Something to remember me by."

"That's it?" He was surprised at how calm he was.

"That's it." She patted his cheek.

"Getting dangerous?"

She looked at him for a moment. "I guess you get it. You're growing up."

"You like me. You don't want to get stuck on me."

"That, and it could get risky for me. And for you, too."

He gave her a little kiss. "Okay. One last time."

She shook her head. "No can do. Stopping means stopping now."

He kissed her again, just a brush on the cheek. "Thank you, Tillie."

She gave him a big smile. "Thank you, Abe."

The next week, Lila was back. Abe felt a little funny about things. When he was leaving, she said, "I told you, kid."

He said, "What could I do?"

She stood in the doorway, her hands on her hips. "You was lucky. Her friends were talking. Your boss knows."

"How?" He didn't like that.

"She got a big mouth. You was her prize. What's the good of having a prize if your friends don't know about it?"

He took a deep breath. Mr. Grossman hadn't said anything. "Okay, I'm going to be more careful."

She walked right up to him. "You better. But someday, if you in the mood, I know stuff she never knew people does."

He was shocked. She laughed and shut the door behind him.

13. That's Better

Estelle knew right away. They were doing the dishes and she sang, "Abie, Abie, this is my answer true . . ."

"Never mind."

"I'd be crazy to marry a fool like you."

They both laughed. He said, "Just wipe the dishes."

"Who was it?"

"None of your beeswax."

"Just as long as one of those husbands doesn't show up. Ma would have a fit."

Abe smiled a big satisfied smile. "That stuff's over and done with."

She thought, *Not for me. Not yet.* "Maybe you can tell me a few tricks." He didn't like that at all.

Confidential tone, but not quite. "You're too young for that stuff, Estelle."

"I'm thirteen. Girls grow up fast these days."

He shook his head, worried. "Girls can get into terrible trouble."

"Okay." She let him off the hook. "Don't worry. I'm only teasing. Can't you tell?"

He was still upset. "I know you, Estelle."

"And I know you, Abe."

"So?"

"So I'm not as dumb as you think I am."

He couldn't resist spelling it out. "Just don't go too far."

Nuts to him, she thought. "What's too far, Abe? Like you do?"

"It's different for men."

"How?"

"Estelle, just don't go too far."

"I won't," she said. "Don't worry."

14. Hard Times

For fifteen years, Morris left for the bakery at four-thirty in the morning and came home at three-thirty in the afternoon, until the day he came home at six in the morning and told Reva that he had been fired.

He handed her a pay envelope. "The boss told us that we couldn't compete with Tastee and Wonder. He gave us a week's salary and wished us luck. That's it. Is there coffee?"

He was still sitting at the table in his uniform when the kids woke up. He didn't say anything to them; they didn't ask. After they left for school, he went to his bedroom and took off the uniform. When the kids came home from school, he was at the table again reading the *Forvertz*.

After three days of sitting in the kitchen and listening to the radio in the living room, he got up after his coffee and left the house. He came back for dinner. This was his routine for two weeks. Where did he go? Reva did not know. Nor did she know where they would get money. Did he care? She didn't know. But finally she had to say, "Morris, you need to work. We need money."

He had a way of making himself seem to shrink. "Reva, I'll dig ditches for the city."

She cried. He left the house.

She kept after him until he said, "There's no jobs. I ain't standing in no line when there's no jobs."

One evening, he came home while the kids were still eating baked beans from dented cans. They could smell the beer on him. It was more than Reva could stand. She said, "You're drinking, and I can't pay the grocery bill."

He let out an awful little laugh and said, "You need money to pay the grocer? Wiggle your ass at Ginsberg."

He looked at her like a crazy man and then at Abe and Estelle who were staring at him.

She said, "Nice. In front of the kids."

Morris drew his head into his chest. He waved his fists like he was having a fit. He said, "You think they don't know about you?"

She could see that he wasn't in control of himself. She said, "Forget it. Do what you want."

Too late. He yelled, "You and the kids need money? Go to their father."

She screamed at him, "I can't! He's dead."

Abe jumped up and ran toward Morris like he was going to hit him. Morris raised his arms. He was going to hit back. Abe stopped and punched the air. He shouted, "No!" and ran out of the house.

No more holding back now. She said to Morris. "You were never a man."

He said, "You never showed me respect."

Estelle put her head on the table and said, "Mommy, Mommy."

Reva told her, "I needed a man."

Estelle didn't hear her.

15. Okay

"Abe, do you think it's true?"

"Yes."

"Why do you think so?"

"We don't look like him. And he's short."

"Lots of kids have one parent who's short."

"He never cared about us."

"Neither did she."

"Yes, she did. Something was in the way. But she cared, in her way. He didn't care."

"He hates us."

"Yes."

"I hate him."

"Me too."

"Abe?"

"What?"

"Can we find out who it was?"

"I think I know."

"Abe! Who?"

"Maybe . . . Dan . . ."

"Abe! Really? How can you know?"

"He really liked us."

"That doesn't mean he's . . . the one."

"It was the way he looked at you once. I thought it then . . . once, but I thought it was impossible. But I thought it then . . . at that time . . . for a moment . . . I did."

"Oh, Abe!"

"Yeah. Dan. I think so. He cared about us."

"I wish I had known."

"Yeah."

"Abe?"

"What?"

"How could they know each other? When could they . . . do it?"

"It's a neighborhood. She used to dress up and go out a lot . . . in the afternoons."

"But . . . he was at the drugstore."

"He could go out for a while if he wanted . . . and he and his wife . . . you know . . . they didn't seem . . . and maybe even if he cared about his wife, he could still . . . And mom could . . . she liked to go out . . . and men noticed her . . . I saw that."

"Abe . . ."

"What?"

"Once I called him daddy."

"You did not."

"I wanted to."

"It's not the same."

"Abe . . ."

"What?"

"I feel okay if it was him."

"Me too."

"Abe . . ."

"What?"

"What's going to happen?"

"I don't know . . . Maybe he'll find work."

"What if he doesn't?"

"You'll have to get a job."

"I'm only thirteen."

"Plenty of kids thirteen have a job. They have to."

"I hate him."

"He's no good."

"Maybe he'll leave."

"He has nowhere to go."

"Abe, I wish I was still little."

"Those days are past."

"I wish they weren't."

"You'll have plenty of good times ahead."

"Do you think so?"

"I know so. You'll see."

"I hope you're right."

"I am."

"Thank you, boyfriend."

"Good night, girlfriend."

"Oh, Abe."

16. Trouble

Abe could see that Irish kids looked different than Jewish kids. Timothy Ryan was thin, had freckles and red hair. He was wiry. He was short. His arms were skinny, but Abe knew he liked to fight. And he certainly liked to talk. He could talk your foot off while Estelle was getting dressed in the bedroom and the two of them were sitting at the kitchen table.

"So, Abe, how's the kosher meat business?"

"Same as any meat business."

"Except for the ham. You people don't know what you're missing. I gotta get you to eat Virginia ham one day."

"At least we don't have to eat fish on Friday."

"You got a point there. I may convert."

"How's the funeral business?"

"Hey, I'm not going to do that crap. Let my brothers do it. I don't like it."

"It's steady."

"If you like corpses. Laying them out. Ugh. I'm going to law school."

"What about college? How can you afford college?"

"I'll skip college. I'll go nights at the Detroit School of Law. I'll work days. I think I have the gift of gab a lawyer needs. Right?"

"A lot of people don't like Irish."

"Who cares? I'm gonna convert and be a Jewish lawyer."

"You do have a gift of gab. And you're nuts. I can't figure out why Estelle likes you."

"I treat her good."

"Yeah."

"Whadya mean?"

"Just be careful."

"Hey, I wouldn't let nothing happen to her."

"Just be careful. If anything happens, you'll have to deal with me."

"Hey, Abe. I thought we were having a friendly talk."

"We were. Just be careful. That's all I'm saying."

"Maybe you'll get the Purple Gang after me."

"I don't need them."

"Aw right, Abe. I wouldn't do nothin' to Estelle. Don't look at me like that. I wouldn't."

Estelle began to come home late at night, nine o'clock, ten o'clock. Morris had gotten a job on the assembly line in the Cadillac plant on East Grand Boulevard. Nights he stayed out, which suited the family. Reva was usually gone in the evenings, visiting with neighbors, going to the movies that she could afford now, anything to stay out of the house. Abe couldn't make Estelle come home early, but he wanted to know what she was doing. He was in bed and awake when she came home at eleven thirty. He could hear her humming a song and said, "Hi." She came around the screen.

"So where do you and Timothy go to at night?"

"I didn't know you were awake, Abe."

"I couldn't sleep."

"You're not my father, Abe."

"I'm more than your father, Estelle."

"Leave me alone, Abe."

"You're all I got, Estelle. I'm all you got."

"We've got to get out of here, Abe."

"We have nowhere to go, not yet. But I have a plan."

"What?"

"I make decent money, forty-five cents an hour and tips, and I'm putting some aside. I can quit school and get another job. We could get our own place."

"Abe, you can't quit school. You have only a year more."

"Where do you go?"

"We go dancing. We love dancing. Wherever it is. He's a great dancer."

"You know those dances?"

"The Lindy, the Charleston, the Foxtrot. Do you know who the Castles were?"

"No."

"They were great dancers. Famous. We want to be like them."

"Dancing . . . ?"

"That's it."

"I was worried."

"You want to see me dance?"

"Sure."

She stood and began to hum and dance around the room, his beautiful sister. She finished by twirling and sitting on his bed. "Good night, Abe."

He said, "Okay, thanks for the show. Good night."

17. What's Wrong with Me, Abe?

Abe, I try to think what's the matter with me. I ask myself why do I do things that other girls would never do. At least, nice girls. Abe, you said, "Don't listen to yourself, Estelle." You said, "Think, Estelle, what would I say? Listen to my voice that is inside of you."

I tried, Abe. Remember that time with Nutty Moie? I still think about that. Why did I go with him? I knew you wouldn't want me to. It's not like I didn't know that. But my voice was stronger. And my voice said, "Go with him, and see what happens."

Then Nutty Moie wouldn't listen to me, he was listening to his voice that said pile coal on that girl. And I could see that Nutty Moie wasn't going to listen to me at all. And I thought that's the way it is. He is not going to stop. Unless Abe comes. I thought, "Abe, where are you?"

You didn't come. I thought when you find out, you'll really be mad at Nutty Moie.

The thing is, Abe, I felt okay. Really. I felt the coal pressing me down. I felt like I couldn't breathe. But I didn't cry. And I didn't yell. Not just because I knew it wouldn't do any good because Nutty Moie was breathing real loud and was piling coal as much as he could. But because it was okay. I didn't mind it. I thought, well, so this is what it's like. Not just having coal piled on me, but having everything go dark. And nobody knows. And nobody but Abe cares. Ma and Pa won't care. They won't even notice if I don't come home. Especially him. But she won't care either. And that's okay, too.

The thing is, Abe, I don't care what happens. Is that terrible? But really, Abe, what's the difference? When I was little, I used to pretend that you would marry me, and I would be safe. Because you were all I had. So then when you wanted other women, what could I do?

Tim Ryan liked me. We had fun, even though he said, "What if your brother finds out," and I knew you would be so mad at me. But it was all I could think that I wanted. I thought, I have Tim, and he likes me, and he'll take care of me. I just wanted to be safe, Abe. Safe from myself, safe from not caring, safe from people who don't care. Because in fact, I don't care. Do you understand me, Abe? Abe, it's okay. This is okay. Really. This is better. I really don't care. Abe, I feel so weak . . .

18. End of the World

That day, Abe could not match what happened with what preceded it. He had kibitzed with customers and flirted with Mrs. Frank who was making eyes at him. He gave Mrs. Farber a little extra ground beef because her husband was on the dole, and she was trying to stretch her pennies to feed seven kids. She saw what he was doing and was teary-eyed; he waved off her silent thanks. Six o'clock, Grossman locked up, and Abe walked home. He turned the corner, saw the crowd in front of his house and then the ambulance, and stopped where he was.

In the flat, Reva was on the couch in the living room, crying, rocking back and forth, holding her head. She did not look at Abe. Morris sat at the kitchen table, not seeing. An ambulance man in a white uniform said, "You family?"

Abe nodded.

"Where do you want her took?"

"What?" Abe stared at him. He could not assemble the man's words into an understandable question. He smiled.

Another man in a similar white uniform came out of Abe and Estelle's bedroom. "Well?" he said to the first man.

"I can't get through to them," the man said.

"Maybe they don't speak English," his partner said. "Maybe we got to get someone here to talk to them in Yiddish."

"No," Abe said.

The first man attempted to sound sympathetic. "Look, mister, we're just doing a job. We need to know what to do with the young lady. Do you want her took to the morgue or to a funeral home?"

Abe felt frozen, as if his heart had stopped beating, his blood no longer circulating. He had to make an amazing effort to get the words out, "What happened?"

The man said, "Coroner's in there," gesturing toward the bedroom. "He'll tell you."

Abe would not go into the bedroom. "Please. Could he come here?"

A short man emerged from the bedroom, shaking his head. He wore a three-piece black suit, a gold chain across his vest and a watch on a gold chain in his watch fob. He had not taken off his black derby hat.

The man fixed on Abe. "Family?"

He nodded.

"I'm Dr. Schmidt, Wayne County coroner." He squeezed his eyes almost shut. "Death was due to massive hemorrhaging subsequent to a botched abortion."

The first ambulance attendant, assuming he had established a connection with Abe, pursued his problem in what he believed was a sympathetic voice. "So, mister, we need to know where do you want her took. Do you know what I mean?"

Abe turned away from him and shook his head slowly. He could not answer.

"Mister," the attendant was urgent. "I'm sorry for your loss. But we got to know what to do with her."

"We'll keep her here," Morris said.

The coroner spoke to him. "You'll have to call the Hebrew Memorial Chapel, I think that's the funeral home you people use, and order a coffin. And make whatever arrangements you want for . . . your . . . for the young person."

Morris would not identify Estelle as his daughter. He did not speak. The coroner was vexed. "Sir?"

Abe spoke now. "I'll do it."

The coroner turned to him. "Very well, sir." Then he said to the ambulance men, "We can leave, gentlemen. There's nothing more for us to do here."

When they were gone, Morris said, "I don't pay for no funeral."

Abe hated him. "I'll take care of it."

Morris glared. "You better go sit with your mother."

Reva was holding herself and bending back and forth. Her face was splotched. She had pulled out the bobby pins in her hair, and it was loose around her shoulders. She looked at Abe and looked away. She murmured, "Baby, baby, my baby . . ." He sat beside Reva on the couch, taking her hand, but not speaking. What was there to say?

In the evening, the Hebrew Chapel people arrived. Abe, Reva and Morris were waiting at the kitchen table. A solemn-looking middle-aged man, Mr. Stein, introduced himself. He wore a black suit and gray tie and a black fedora. Two old women, dressed in black, went into the bedroom and shut the door. Stein explained. "They're Chevra Kadisha."

Morris and Reva nodded. Abe didn't understand.

"The Holy Society," Stein said. "They wash and dress her in a shroud and comb her hair. It's a mitzvah."

"A good deed," Abe said.

"They're appointed by their rabbi. It's the ultimate charitable act," Stein explained. "It can never be repaid. Only the most deserving can be Chevra Kadisha."

Reva suddenly stood and left the room. After a few minutes she came back with a package wrapped in tissue paper and tied with twine. She put the package on the table, unwrapped it and held up a white long-sleeved linen garment.

Stein nodded. "From the old country."

"My mother sewed it. It was the last thing she gave me. In those days, there was no time to make a shroud . . . if the angel of death called suddenly . . . you never knew."

Stein took the shroud. He rapped on the bedroom door, said something quietly and handed the garment to the Chevra Kadisha women.

After a short while, one of them went into the bathroom and emerged with a large bowl of water.

Reva said, "A midwife carried in water when she was born."

The doorbell rang. "That's our men," Stein said. Four men, black caps on their heads, carried a plain pine coffin up the stairs, into the living room and left.

The family and Stein sat drinking tea, not speaking. After thirty minutes, the two old women came out of the bedroom carrying Estelle, whom they had wrapped in the shroud, down the hall past the kitchen and into the living room. Stein followed them and shut the door. Reva sat upright, tears trickling down her cheeks. Morris jumped up and left the room. They heard him go down the stairs. Abe closed his eyes and softly pounded the kitchen table. Stein looked into the kitchen. "I'm sorry," he said. "She's ready. Do you want it left open or closed?"

Reva looked at Abe. He said, "Closed."

"Do you want to see her first?" Stein said.

Abe shook his head. "No."

Reva stood. "I do." She remained in the living room for about fifteen minutes. When she returned to the kitchen, she walked in a swaying glide, her legs stiff.

Stein went back to the living room to close the coffin. When he returned, in a soft voice he said, "Do you want us to post a notice about shiva in the Chronicle? We don't have to name the cause of death."

Abe nodded. "Please, and thank you."

"You've been helpful," Reva said.

Stein nodded. "Are you able to talk about the other arrangements?"

They looked at him.

He said, "About the burial? She should be buried tomorrow. And about the rabbi."

"What do we do?" Abe said. "We don't belong to a synagogue."

"We can arrange for the rabbi," Stein said. "And we can obtain a plot in Mach Pelah on Woodward Avenue. It's not expensive, and it's well-maintained."

"Thank you," Abe said. "I'm sorry. I'm not thinking."

"Of course," Stein said. He looked apologetic. "There's one more matter to take care of."

A change in his tone signaled Abe about what was coming. "The payment," Stein said. He became brisk. "I'm sorry to have to raise this topic now, in your grief." He shrugged and sighed. "We have different plans according to your means. You can pay in one payment or you can take advantage of our installment plan."

Abe said, "One payment. How much?"

Stein nodded. "One payment is the best way. Our fee is $230 with the coffin and transportation to Mach Pelah. That doesn't include the rabbi's fee, of course, which shouldn't be much . . . they're all so poor. And also a small donation to Chevra Kadisha, something nominal."

Abe shuddered. Stein closed his eyes and rocked several times heel to toe.

Reva said, "I'm going to sit with her."

"I will too," Abe said.

Stein pursed his lips. "That's fine. We'll have one of our licensed people sit with you. It's the law. I have a young man who will be unobtrusive . . . We'll send the hearse at nine in the morning. Is there anything else I can do?"

They shook their heads.

"Please accept my deepest sympathy and condolences," Stein said and left.

Reva and Abe, along with Stein's young man who sat in a corner and read his Bible, kept Estelle company on her last night above ground, thinking their own thoughts, grieving silently and apart. Morris returned at first light, looked into the living room and went to his bedroom without speaking. They did not care where he had been.

Other than family and Reva's cousin, Sonya, only the Goodmans and Meyer Grossman and his wife, Edna, and Stein attended the graveside service. Two gravediggers stood a short distance away, but close enough to hear the rabbi who had been told of the untimely death and who said, in a sad voice, that Estelle's time on earth had been a joy to all who knew her, but that now God, in His wisdom, had decided to take her to Him. Nobody else spoke. Abe wanted to, but couldn't. He mumbled the Kaddish by following the rabbi's words. When he threw a clump of dirt on the coffin, his knees buckled. Stein and Meyer Grossman held him up.

Reva and Abe kept shiva for the seven days. Neighborhood acquaintances came, awkward. Morris returned home only to sleep. The Goodmans were there all the time and brought food, roast chicken, brisket, noodle kugel, salads of peas and beans, rye bread, dill pickles and coleslaw from the delicatessen, ginger ale and Coca-Cola. School friends of Estelle brought cakes and candy. Meyer Grossman sent a large platter of cold cuts. Reva's sister, Rae, came from Chicago and, along with cousin Sonya, helped in the kitchen and cleaned the flat.

The family talked about Estelle. Sonya recalled the time when Estelle was sick with pneumonia. Reva talked about Abe helping to take care of his little sister. Rae said, "She loved to play with jacks." The Goodmans talked about Estelle staying with them when Abe had scarlet fever. He did not speak. He tried to be polite and look like he was listening, but could not bring himself to talk about his sister.

After a time, nobody talked to him. Nobody mentioned Pa. The living room became silent. *Like it always was*, Abe thought.

On the fourth day, in the early evening, Rae remarked on a young goy who was standing across the street. "Every day, I see him when I come. He doesn't move."

Abe clenched his fists and went outside to face Timothy Ryan who was staring up at the windows of the flat, his hands in his jacket pockets.

Timothy did not look at him, but said, "Can I come up?"

Abe shuddered. "No. You don't belong."

"Are you going to kill me?"

"No."

"Why not? I thought you would."

Abe said, "Go home." He put his hand on Timothy's chest and pushed him back two steps.

Timothy stood still; he did not remove his hands from his pockets. He said in a quiet voice, "I loved her."

Abe shook his head. "No."

"We were going to get married."

"No."

"She said she loved me."

"No."

"I don't know what to do, Abe."

Abe exploded. "You killed her! You killed her! I told you to be careful. You knew her. You knew she would never stop herself."

Timothy sat on the sidewalk, his head leaning over and touching the cement. "Oh, Jesus, oh, my Lord who art in heaven."

Abe went back into the house.

19. The Rest of My Life

Reva could not talk about Estelle. She thought, *What am I going to do with the rest of my life? Rae says that I should come to her in Chicago. I may as well. I have nothing here to hold me.*

There was a terrible fire on Reva's block. Two children were playing with matches. Their father was asleep. The mother was out. The curtains in the living room caught fire. Both kids died along with their father who was trying to save them. People said that the mother was visiting a friend, a man friend. Her life is ruined. She has not spoken since the fire.

Reva could understand her not talking. What could she say? She did not know her, but could not help comparing their fates. She thought, *Sometimes you make a mistake, which leads to another mistake, and another, and you are lost. Dan and I fell into each other's arms. We were meant for each other. He was the love of my life. He said that marrying his wife was the mistake of his life. But she was sick, and he could not leave her. Also, they could not have babies. It wasn't his problem as we discovered. But then I had to find a husband.*

She knew Morris because their families lived in the same shtetl in the Ukraine. They met in their landsmanshaft storefront on Hastings Street. Because of his twisted leg, Morris had not expected to marry or have a family. He was the innocent of innocents with women. He held Reva, and she told him of her loneliness. Within a week, they spent the night together. Morris felt like he imagined that a man should feel. They married quickly. She did her best to please him. For six months, he was happy. But then he understood about Abe, her big fine healthy baby boy, and he hated her because he knew that she had trapped him. He hated Abe, then Estelle, her poor sweet children; how could they understand? Poor Morris. Poor Reva. Doomed.

What could she have done? What?

20. Goodbye, Mother

Within two weeks, Abe moved out. He rented a room for $2.25 a week in a house a few blocks away. One night, his landlady, Mrs. Baum, knocked on his door and told him that his mother had come. He went to the door of the flat. Reva was standing in the hall in a housecoat and slippers. Her hair was hanging down, tangled. She wore no makeup. "Abe," she said in a whisper.

He led her to his room. She sat in his one chair; he sat on the bed. She told him that she was going to live with her sister, Rae, in Chicago. They sat without talking.

After a while, Reva sighed and said," Do you hate me, Abe?"

He shook his head. "I don't know."

"I needed . . . to live."

Abe said, "Why didn't you talk to us?"

Reva stared at him. "Talk to you?"

"Yeah."

"About what?"

He jumped up and stood over her. "About what? About anything. About us. About your life. About our father."

Reva went white. "Abe!"

"Morris was an animal. You knew better. You didn't try."

"I was trapped," she said.

"Trapped?"

"In the silence."

"What?"

"It was a quiet house. It was how it was. I couldn't help it. I was stuck in it. Can you understand?"

"You should have tried."

Reva stood. "I hope I see you again, Abe."

He shook his head. "I doubt it. I don't know."

"Goodbye, Abe."

"Goodbye, Mother."

21. Abe and Helen

Women: there were plenty and available for anything he wanted, dancing, home-cooked meals, talking, peace and quiet, willing to be in bed with him, all of them, any of them just waiting for him to take the next step.

So what was big, handsome Abe waiting for? Didn't he want to marry, lead a regular life with a wife and little kids waiting for him at home? What did he want? Abe didn't know. But he wasn't ready, that he knew.

In the butcher shop, his workers kibitzed. "Hey, Abe, the customers are fainting. They only want for you to wait on them. Give us a break, Abe. Choose one. Any one. What about Lois Fine? Gorgeous, a winner. Shirley Gold, what a body. I'll take her if you won't, but my Zelda would kill me. Pearl Zimmerman, Abe. Personality, fun and goo-goo eyes she's making at you. Helen Schwartz, Abe. A nice girl. Maybe not exciting, but steady, a comfortable woman, a true Jewish mate. And, Abe's workers wouldn't say it, but they all knew that Helen was a virgin. Joey, who years ago had helped to train Abe, had been heard to say, "She may as well have a sign on her back: virgin here, waiting for wedding bed, thank you very much."

And gradually, somehow, a consensus grew among Abe's staff and valued customers that he should begin to notice Helen, really notice her. It seemed to Abe, without anything being said, that the whole world was pushing him at her. All he had to do was to say the word. But the word stuck in his throat.

What about Helen? Pretty? Almost. Good figure? Not bad. But if she was longing for Abe, you couldn't tell it. She was offhand and polite, even distant, which used to aggravate him.

When he handed her a package of chopped meat and held her hand longer than necessary, she smiled sweetly, lifted his hand from hers and said, "Thank you, Abe," and left the store.

Then what happened? Well, Abe was intrigued enough to persist. He asked Helen on dates to movies, to dinner, and, best of all, to dancing at clubs where the big bands played. She was a good dancer and taught him new steps, and he loved that.

Abe was still reserved when they said goodnight on her doorstep; he didn't lay a hand on her. Why? He asked himself why. Because, he told himself, she was different, still inside, calm. She kept her distance, though she enjoyed his stories and laughed with him.

Gradually, without thinking of sex, much less about marriage, he began to relax with her, even to take her for granted, a pal. He began to tell her about pa with his limp and ma who liked to put on rouge and lipstick and flirt in the neighborhood. And both ma and pa always silent around Abe and his little sister, Estelle. As if there were nothing to say, nothing to share, no interest in their kids lives.

What about Helen? To Abe, she was uninteresting. "I had a good time," she said. "I had a best friend, Gloria. We played jacks and walked around and looked at people and wondered what life would be like when we grew up."

"What about your parents?" he wondered.

"They were just parents," she told him. "They watched out for us and took us on vacations, and worried if we were sick. Just parents. Nothing like what you went through. You had a terrible childhood." And now she put her hand on his arm and kept it there. "I don't know what kept you going."

"What kept me going," he told her, "was Estelle. She needed me. I was strong. I knew what ma and pa were like. She hated them, but didn't know what to do. I held her up. We were there for each other."

"Then she died," Helen said. "After the abortion."

"She died," Abe agreed. "And I didn't want to live any more. I didn't feel like I had anything to live *for*."

Helen turned away from him and cried into her handkerchief. He saw that and wanted to reach out for her, but still he held back. "Not yet," he told himself. Then he thought, "Nobody's going to believe this. Big Abe. Ladies' man. Yeah. Big shot. Right? Not with this girl, not now." Then he thought, "How long am I going to stay with this plain Jane? Maybe I should start to see other women again."

Helen felt him pull away. She stood in front of him, staring. Then she grabbed him. They kissed hard. She sobbed. He groaned.

Later, she teased, "I didn't know you were so shy."

He admitted, "I couldn't get started."

"Maybe I reminded you of your sister," she said.

He thought about this. "I think you're right," he said. "And that's good and bad."

"Don't worry," she said. "I won't tell anyone."

Part Three:
The Nollman Family

1. The Bank Story

Charlie Nollman was nine years old when his father died. His ma, Naomi, had to support the family, Charlie and his three older sisters, Lena, Matilda and Susie. Their big shot uncles told Naomi to open a hand laundry. With such cheap labor, they said (they were talking about the kids) you needed only a little capital: *gournisht*, nothing. For three hundred dollars, Uncle Moe had it figured out, they could be in business with a few large sinks, some wooden drying racks, hand irons, long tables, a hot water heater that ran on coal that you could also heat the irons on and a barrel of laundry soap. What else? An empty store on a side street. There were plenty to choose from.

To get the three hundred dollars, the big shot uncles told Naomi to go to the bank on Houston Street.

"Good idea," she said. "I'll go." She was afraid of nothing.

But the kids thought, *Oy vey. With her accent.*

Matilda, who was not the most practical, said, "Maybe the man will be Jewish."

Susie laughed at her. "Dummy, all bankers are goyim."

That's when Lena said, "I have a plan. Charlie . . ."

The plan was for Charlie to explain to the man if Ma got *ferblungit.*

"Bad idea," he said. "I'm too little."

"You're little," they said, "but you're smart. You know numbers. And you're not a woman."

"What if I forget?" he said.

They said, "Why do you worry so much? We'll tell you everything you need to know, and we'll be right there with you."

So the morning they were going to the bank, Lena and Matilda handed Charlie new corduroy knickers, long black stockings that were held up by garters at his knees, a new white shirt and a clip-on red bow tie that he loved.

He yelled at them, "Where did you get this stuff?"

They laughed. "Just don't get it dirty, Charlie. It all has to go back to the store."

They didn't know that he was never going to let them return that bow tie. He still has it.

Anyway, the Nollmans, Naomi in her black dress and black stockings, the girls in their High Holiday clothes, Charlie looking spiffy in his new outfit, stood outside the bank with its big granite columns and glass doors that were twice as tall as people.

"This could have been the czar's palace," Lena said. "Let's go." In a nervous clump, they walked in, pushing at each other, touching each other.

They walked on big squares of white marble. The walls were marble, too, the same color as the floor, all the way up to the ceiling. The ceiling, when they looked up, was a dome of glass. The sun shining through it made everything yellow.

They felt better when they saw that a lot of the customers were Jews, but they didn't know whom to talk to. They looked around until Lena pointed to a man behind a desk with a sign that said Loan Officer.

Susie was right. The man was a goy, with straight blond hair combed across his head. He looked at them standing in front of his desk and said, "Can I help you?"

Naomi was raring to go. She started her spiel with the kids standing in a line behind her. Right away they could see that the man was not understanding her. How could he? How could anyone? Naomi spoke two languages-Yiddish to other Jews, and Yinglish to goyim. But when she was done, he said, "A laundry, is it?"

He had heard the word *laundry*. Naomi thought that he had understood her. She stood there like a peacock and stuck out her hand. She thought he was going to hand her the money. But he had a strange look on his face and didn't say anything. She waited. He waited. Lena pushed Charlie from behind. He bumped into Naomi who said, "Leiber Gott," and pushed him away. Lena pushed him forward again. Charlie cleared his throat, but couldn't speak.

Lena said, "Talk to the man."

Matilda said, "Charlie, we need the money."

Susie said, "Charlie, tell him or I'll kill you."

So Charlie said, "Sir, I would like to explain."

The man held up his hand. "Would you like a piece of candy?"

Charlie looked at Lena. She shook her head no.

"No, sir," he said.

Naomi said, "Vous? Vous?"

Lena said, "Ma, shah. Charlie is telling him."

Naomi was mad now. "Didn't I just tell him?"

All three girls yelled, "Ma, shah!"

Naomi looked like she was going to yell back at them. They shook their heads no. She was really mad. She stood there talking to herself.

Charlie got started again. He told the man about the laundry and that they needed only three hundred dollars.

The man smiled. "Very good. I understand. A hand laundry. And you need only three hundred dollars."

Charlie turned to the girls and laughed. They patted him on the head. Naomi didn't like it. She headed for the door. The man said, "Madam, don't you want the money?"

She turned around, came back, leaned over his desk, and held out her hand again.

"Madam," he said, "you and your son explained very well, but there is a little more we have to talk about."

"Vous?" Naomi said.

Now the man leaned over his desk and said slowly and as clearly as he could, "Can you get someone to cosign for the loan?"

He could see that they didn't know what *cosign* meant, and he explained that someone had to sign the loan papers with them. Then if the business failed, the person who cosigned would pay back the loan.

"That's it?" Charlie said.

"That's it," the man said.

They were quiet for a moment. They all had the same thought. They didn't know anyone who could cosign. Charlie said, "I'll take the candy," and they walked out of the bank.

What happened then? The next few days, they discussed the situation. And that's when Susie solved the problem. She was a gorgeous girl. All three sisters were gorgeous. And it turned out that Susie, once in a while, not often, she told them, but once in a while even though she was only fifteen, would go into a place called Smith's Saloon that was across the street from the Essex Street Market, their big meat, fish, vegetable, fruit, bread, bagel, pastry and delicatessen market.

Even Charlie knew about Smith's Saloon that was owned by a big-time Jew who called himself Silver Dollar Smith. Actually, Charlie had heard that the floor of the saloon was paved with silver dollars. Personally, he didn't believe it and asked Susie who said, "Don't be silly."

Anyway, it turned out that Susie had met a man whose name was Arnold Rothstein.

Susie was so nervy that she had gotten to know Arnold Rothstein who then was a young guy already famous as a gambler. Arnold Rothstein, it turned out, liked Susie. And listen to this, she told her family that Arnold Rothstein had said that he was going to watch out for her and that nobody should pester her. He told everybody in the place to respect Susie like he did because, he said, she reminded him of his dead sister, if you can believe that. Susie swore it was true. The other kids almost fainted.

So the next day, when she mentioned the family's problem to her friend, Arnold Rothstein, just like that he said that he would come to the bank and cosign for the loan.

Back they went. And the man stared at Arnold Rothstein who was wearing a diamond stickpin that looked like it was worth much more than the loan.

"No problem," the man told them. "No problem at all." So Arnold Rothstein cosigned for the loan. And that's how the Nollmans started the hand laundry.

2. Not So Funny

Well, listen now, the Nollmans talk about the old days as if they were funny, as if they had a lot of laughs. They didn't have such a good time. What do you think Naomi thought when Susie told them that she goes into Smith's Saloon? Fifteen years old! What was she doing in such a place? A nice Jewish girl. Naomi said that Pa would have killed her. Naomi wanted to kill her. But she didn't. She just stood there and didn't say a word.

Naomi knew about saloons. There were taverns in Russia. There were Jewish tavern keepers. When the Cossacks came, the families hid their daughters in the basement of these taverns. So Naomi didn't care what business Arnold Rothstein was in.

Which brings us back to the bank. How do you think the Nollmans felt walking into that place? The girls looked like they were sleepwalking. Charlie wanted to throw up. Naomi was talking to herself even before the man made her mad. None of the kids understood how she had the guts to talk to him. Especially with the look on his face. To them, he looked like he wanted to laugh. Out loud. But he didn't. And later, they had to admit he listened, and who could understand Naomi's Yinglish?

Also, to the kids, the man behind his desk looked like a giant. When he leaned over to talk to Naomi, they thought he must be ten feet tall; he leaned over so far. They couldn't believe it.

But when Arnold Rothstein walked in, the man didn't seem so tall. And they couldn't help feeling proud of Arnold Rothstein and proud that he was their friend, at least Susie's friend. Though on the other hand, when they left the bank, and Arnold Rothstein put his hand on Susie's shoulder. and she was laughing at what he was telling her, none of them, especially Naomi, was happy about that.

Later, much later, Charlie told them why he had had trouble talking to the man. He said, "It was the first time in my life, outside of school, that I ever talked to a grown-up goy."

He had thought, *How can I do this? I have never been a religious person, but I prayed, please, God of the Jews, give me strength.*

Anyway, the Nollmans started the laundry business. And everyone had to help. Even Susie, though some evenings when she walked out of the store, none of the others asked where she was going.

But then years later, when they told Susie that they had been worried about whom she was associating with, she said, "Me? I was a nothing in that place. They thought it was funny to have me carry steins of beer to the cops. The first time I thought I would die. I was scared they were going to put me in jail. But the cops just looked at me and laughed. And they gave me big tips. So Smith and them used to let me hang around. That's all. I hung around. When it got late, they sent me home. I was so embarrassed."

"So, Susie," Charlie said to her, "what if we didn't pay our loan to the bank? Did you ever worry about that?"

And she said, "Arnold Rothstein wouldn't have liked that. He didn't like welshers." So they thought about that for a moment. "Anyway," she said, "Ma wouldn't let that happen. You know how she ran that business."

Naomi had her own system of keeping the books, scribbling numbers on both sides of scraps of paper that she kept in a drawer. And she was tough with the customers. If they didn't pay right away, she sold their stuff, even when they cried and begged her to be easy with them, even when the sisters begged her. "Ma," they would say, "she's a good person. Ma, her husband had a little bad luck. Ma, he needs the shirts for his work. Let him make a little money so they can pay us."

"Zoll zein, sha," Naomi would say to get us to shut up, and that was that.

So Naomi was funny, right? Sometimes she dropped cigarette ashes on the clean sheets and shirts.

"Ma, be careful," the girls said.

"Nisht gefarlacht. Don't bother yourself," she would say, blowing the ashes away.

Life in the tenement was funny, right? Even the Nollmans laugh now when Charlie tells how his sisters grabbed food off the table before he could get to it because he was small and didn't need to eat so much. But now, he said, Susie has a chauffeur, for God's sake. And the chauffeur has plenty to eat. In those days, he said, how many times did he drink seltzer to fill his stomach? And go to bed gassy? Which was nothing to laugh at when there were three other people in the bed, and they yelled and poked him in the ribs. A lot of nights Charlie didn't sleep so well. He looks at his grown-up sisters now and says, "I can't help myself. I make it sound funny. But it wasn't." He goes on. "Take the bathroom." When Charlie was ten, they passed a law that made the landlords put two bathrooms on every floor of the tenements, bathrooms with flush toilets. Before that, the family used a privy, a hole in the ground behind the tenement. Talk about smells. Oy vey. Uncle Moe once told them that he always wanted to be constipated. Of course then, the smell would have been twice as terrible. Nice, huh?

Charlie reminded them that his sisters used to razz him about being small. But that didn't stop them from being interested in his thingy. Actually, the truth was that they liked to touch it and watch it get big. Really. When he was ten or eleven, he really said it, he liked it, too.

And then there were the Wasserman sisters, Reva and Minnie, who lived on the floor above them. When the Wasserman girls got older, they were fat.

But then they were just big. Much bigger than he was. When they went out, they put on rouge and lipstick. Lena told Charlie to stay away from them. Of course, whatever his sisters said, he did the opposite.

Reva and Minnie used to complain about their stepfather who wanted to get into bed with them when their ma was out. They liked to tell Charlie about their boyfriends and how far they let them go, sometimes all the way, and he knew what that meant.

He used to meet the sisters on the stairs that led to the roof. Sometimes they would sit on the stair above him and open their legs so he could see their underwear. Once Reva, the youngest, didn't wear any underwear. Charlie started to sweat. He saw his sisters' underwear all the time. But they never did that. Reva saw him sweating and laughed. So did Minnie who started to hit Reva and both them were laughing and then they were kissing each other on the lips. And they grabbed Charlie and kissed him on the lips, and Reva put his hand on her thing. That really made him sweat. And her skirt was around her hips. And he knew that he wouldn't ever forget what happened then, with Reva making noises and Minnie laughing like she would bust. Oh, brother.

After that, he wanted to see his sisters undressed. He couldn't help himself. He had a desire to see them naked. They caught him peeking and yelled. He was embarrassed and swore he wasn't doing it. But they knew better and watched out for him.

3. Lena and the Shadkin

The *shadkins* were clamoring. They accosted Naomi on the street, in the stores, even on the balcony of the little synagogue during the High Holidays. "Mrs. Nollman, listen to me. I have the perfect man for your Lena."

Lena was famous in her Lower East Side neighborhood: a choosy virgin who had become the focus of a shadkin contest. They wouldn't let Naomi alone. "Mrs. Nollman, Mrs. Nollman, listen to me. Don't run away from me, Mrs. Nollman."

Naomi had to yell at Lena. "Listen, Miss Fancypants, you got to choose. The shadkins are driving me crazy. Your sisters are waiting for you to go first. What do you want? For my other daughters to be old maids like you?"

Lena knew that her problem was pride. She could not stand the thought of giving herself away, and for what? A *shmendrick* who would give her babies and make a poor living; she would be back where she started. On Rivington Street wearing shmates and washing diapers.

Lena was tough on herself. "Dummy! So choose. One's the same as the next. You're old. Twenty already. Choose, meshuga. What's the difference?"

The difference, she told herself, was that she was Lena, flower of the Nollman family, the most beautiful of the sisters, also the tallest, the smartest, the quickest, the funniest, the best storyteller and the one her mother sent to the door to confront salesmen.

Which is how she encountered Cohen, a *longaloch*, a tall string bean of a man in a suit two sizes too small, but with a daredevil smile who was waiting for her to answer the doorbell. He sized her up and knew that Lena was no pushover.

"Darling, see what your gorgeous face will look like with my Song of Angels beauty cream."

"Go away."

"On your sweet punim, this cream from heaven will make the angels sing."

"Try the Shifmans next door, bozo. Those girls will shmear on any dreck."

"How come you ain't married, sweetheart?"

"None of your business. Get your shoe out of my door."

Cohen had a knowing look. "You need me, darling. My brother-in-law, Meyerowitz, is an A1 shadkin."

"Shadkins we don't need. They're lined up. Goodbye."

"You know what they say about pride, my belle of the Ukraine."

"Tell Meyerowitz if he comes, I'll have my big brother throw him down the stairs."

"Who's worried? My brother-in-law is also a wrestler."

"My brother is a prize fighter."

"It should be interesting, my turtledove," Cohen said through the closing door.

Lena, after finally shutting him out, trembled despite herself. She believed in destiny, and this salesman had gotten under her skin. She feared the arrival of Meyerowitz who came the very next day and was patiently drinking tea with her mother who was home from the laundry. Lena arrived in the late afternoon after her sales job in Woolworth's.

Meyerowitz, a thin man, never a wrestler, glanced at her over his raised teacup, but talked only to Naomi. "Mrs. Nollman, listen to me. Have I got a man for your Lena."

Lena made a clamor in the sink and could not hear her mother's response. After drinking a glass of water, she was on her way to the room in the back of the tenement where the sisters slept when she heard the name Max Tannenbaum. She ran back and screamed at Meyerowitz, "Who! Who!"

Meyerowitz smiled at Naomi who was blowing into her teacup. "I told you, missus, a prize. Max Tannenbaum, the wealthy manufacturer of women's stylish clothes."

Naomi's eyes lit up. Her main hope in life these days was for her daughters to marry men who would support her. She wanted only to get out of the laundry business. "Tell me," she instructed Meyerowitz.

Lena collapsed on a chair. "Ma," she moaned, "a dwarf. Max Tannenbaum is a dwarf."

Meyerowitz shook his head sadly. "Such a thing to say, darling. Max happens to be five feet five inches tall. With elevator heels, five feet seven." He smiled at Naomi. "Your daughter happens to be a shtarke, praise God. She breathes air that is higher and more pure than the rest of us can hope for."

Naomi was focused on what mattered. "The dress business is good?"

Meyerowitz, a pro, moved in for the kill. "Never better. Your daughter will eat meat every night and every morning grade A extra large eggs." He did not have to mention the side benefits to Naomi.

Lena was on her knees. "Ma," she groaned. "No, Ma, please."

Naomi hadn't gone without all these years for nothing. "Sha," she told Lena. "It's settled." To Meyerowitz, she said, "Bring him tomorrow for dinner."

Lena fainted. Meyerowitz splashed water on her. Naomi didn't care. Lena, on her back, said to Meyerowitz, "Tell him that I'll murder him in our nuptial bed."

Meyerowitz leered. "I ain't worried, darling."

Lena remembered the other thing she had heard about Max Tannenbaum. He liked tall women. As it turned out, he also liked his models.

4. Matilda and Josiah

After her sister, Lena, married Max Tannenbaum, Matilda, the next in line, discovered Josiah Gabrielson sitting alone in a corner at a dance sponsored by the Jewish Center. Matilda swooped in. Soon the two were talking, though she had to carry most of the conversation.

She had been urged on in her campaign by the youngest sister, Susie, who had plans of her own, and by Naomi.

Handsome, though prematurely balding, Josiah had been raised by a doting and jealous mother and was impatient with maternal restraints; his father, an itinerant typesetter, had kept himself far from home and his commanding wife.

Matilda had never met anyone like Josiah who was introspective, wrote poetry and, like many educated young Jews, was an ardent Communist. More to the point, he had just graduated from dental school.

Like her sisters, Matilda was tall and beautiful and used her body, when necessary, to entrap eligible men. She welcomed Josiah into her arms and allowed him to believe that she was madly in love.

Sexstruck, naïve about women, and having devoted himself to his studies, he was happy to escape into marriage, which led Matilda, who was carried away by her success, to believe that he could be easily manipulated.

With their wedding only weeks away, her first indication that he might prove unreasonable was when he told her that he was planning on practicing dentistry in Russia.

Matilda blinked. "Russia? Where our parents left?"

"Yes, that Russia." Josiah pulled a leather-bound volume from his shelf and handed it to Matilda. "You can read about Russia in the *EB*."

"The *EB*?"

"*Encyclopedia Britannica*. Everything I know about the world, I have read in the *EB*."

Matilda reported this development to her sisters.

"Russia?" Lena said. "Why Russia? Is he meshuga?"

Matilda sighed. "He read about Russia in the *Encyclopedia Britannica*, the *EB*."

"The *EB*? Susie said.

"He has read it from cover to cover," Matilda reported.

"Oy," Lena said.

"Vey," Susie agreed with the diagnosis.

"What can I do?" Matilda said. "He is determined."

"What can you do?" Lena said. "You can do what any sensible Jewish girl would do."

Matilda and Josiah touched knees as they sat over glasses of tea and prune Danish in Mandelbaum's Cafeteria. Josiah was gloomy. "Are you certain?"

She was tearful. "Yes, I'm sorry."

He accused her, "When is it due?"

She sobbed. "In seven months. We should have been more careful."

He looked into his teacup and muttered. "You can follow me to Russia with the baby."

"Yes, Josiah," she said in a wistful voice.

"They have excellent nurseries in Russia," he said, reviving. "I have read about them."

She was meek. "Yes, Josiah."

"It's all set then."

"Good," she said and added, "Wait until my family hears about the baby."

She watched him closely, anticipating what was going to happen. Elbows on the table, his head in his hands, Josiah considered his mother's reaction to becoming a grandmother and then to her son taking her grandchild to Russia. Aglow and energized one moment, he now looked collapsed. Matilda felt sorry for him.

"I had no choice," she said afterward to Susie. "How could I go to Russia?"

They were married in a month. Matilda suffered an apparent miscarriage and became depressed. Doctor Katzman insisted that the cure was to become pregnant again. Josiah complied, initiating the first of two successful pregnancies.

In his midtown dental office on Madison Avenue, Josiah wrote poems between patient visits and also completed New York Times crossword puzzles with a fountain pen, a sardonic expression on his face. Observing her sister Lena's loss of Max's attentions to his models, Matilda made sure that Josiah's dental assistants were older women, the plainer the better. She did not understand that these women, too, craved affection and were more than willing to perform activities she had never heard of.

"Who knew?" she complained. "And in the middle of the day."

5. Susie and Sheldon

Susie was seventeen and looked twenty when Sheldon Bergstresser walked into Smith's Saloon one evening in search of a little excitement. Slender, medium height with a neatly trimmed mustache, Sheldon wore bespoken three-piece suits, beige spats over sporty shoes and long black or brown socks that were held up by garters. He fancied a malacca cane. His trademark was a red handkerchief in his breast pocket. He wore silk underwear as she discovered soon after he had won her in a game of table-stakes heads-up poker.

At first, she was upset. "What do you mean you won me?" she yelled. "What am I? A stack of chips?"

"That's it, honey," he said. "You were all Jack had left. Come on." He led the way out of Smith's.

"If my ma finds out, she'll kill me," she said. "Or she'll murder you."

Sheldon wasn't bothered by the odds of this happening. When he wasn't gambling, he developed real estate, including tall buildings in downtown Manhattan. He had already lost two fortunes betting on the horses and recouped just as fast. From the moment he saw Susie, he wanted her. She was pretty enough for him and knew how to dress. She was a wizard with a shears and the Singer. Every cent she could scavenge from odd jobs and her family went into versions of Chanel and Schiaparelli. And Sheldon liked Susie's lively manner. Here was a girl, he saw, who could enjoy herself and at the same time he would like being with. But having won her, he thought, *Easy come, easy go.* And he said, "You want to stay here? Do I care? Goodbye."

"Hold it," she said. "Give me a minute. I have to think, don't I?"

Susie considered. She had enjoyed the respect in Smith's Saloon that came with being Jack Ryan's girlfriend. But that was over. She was not a deep thinker and acted on impulse. And her impulse now was to feel insulted. But she was not stupid and understood that Sheldon Bergstresser had big money written all over him. What is more, she thought, Sheldon was Jewish and if it came to that, she could bring him home. "Oh, well," she said. She tucked her arm through his. "Where are we headed?"

They were headed for a mansion in the Westchester County town of Larchmont, where in the next five years, Susie gave birth to two handsome boys and then a lovely little girl. Susie was driven by a chauffeur in their LaSalle roadster; she flew to Miami Beach and a private box at Hialeah racetrack and to gambling in Cuba with companions like the mobster genius, Meyer Lansky.

Over the years, for Sheldon, other women were incidental for occasional pleasure. Susie didn't mind. She had the life she wanted. So did her mother, Naomi.

6. Naomi versus Shakespeare

Naomi had just left Matilda and Josiah's apartment on West End Avenue in Manhattan to visit Susie and Sheldon in Larchmont. Josiah said, "For a week, your mother will ride around in Sheldon's roadster, smoking her cigarettes and telling his chauffeur where to go until she gets bored. Then she'll go back to the Bronx and make Lena and Max miserable. When she's tired of being there, she'll come here again. Since she closed the laundry, she's been coming and going whenever she feels like it. We have nothing to say about it. Personally, I'm fed up."

Matilda shrugged. "That's Ma. What can we do?"

"It wouldn't be so bad," Josiah said. "But she thinks she can tell us how to run our lives."

"Ma is smart," Matilda said. "She gives me good advice."

"About what?"

"About our marriage."

He did not like where this topic might be headed. "Things were better when she was busy," he said. "How long is this going to go on?"

The following Sunday morning, Josiah, at breakfast, smiled as he spread cream cheese and placed slices of lox, sweet onion and tomato on a plain bagel. Matilda noted that he was nodding his head as if he were agreeing with somebody.

"So who are you agreeing with, Josiah?"

Josiah bit into his bagel and grinned. Bits of cream cheese and lox showed between his front teeth. "With myself," he told her. "I have a wonderful idea."

He chuckled. Matilda couldn't resist deflating him. "Josiah, you shouldn't talk with your mouth full of cream cheese and lox," she said. "It looks terrible."

She was immediately sorry when he frowned and turned away. Since their wedding two years ago, Matilda had made it her business to anticipate her husband's desires and cater to his moods. But once in a while, her resolve cracked and she couldn't resist whacking him in his vulnerable ego.

Now having had her moment of satisfaction, she sighed and said, "So what's your idea?"

Josiah's good spirits resurfaced. He waved a finger while he swallowed the remains of the bagel and said, "Your ma loves the Yiddish theater, right?"

Matilda nodded.

"What we're going to do," he said in a conspiratorial tone, "is to get Max to take her to *The Yiddish King Lear.*"

"*King Lear* by Shakespeare?"

"By Jacob Gordin," he said. "It's based on Shakespeare. Jacob Adler is Lear. Your ma loves Jacob Adler, right?"

"Why do you want to do this?" Matilda said.

Josiah sounded like he was talking to the simple-minded. "*King Lear* is about what happens when the king antagonizes his three daughters and their husbands."

"So?"

"So one daughter runs to France and the other two are fed up, and their husbands turn against Lear. They don't want him to visit. Their doors are shut. Your ma should see this play."

"Doesn't he go blind and die in the end?" she said. "Ma wouldn't like that."

"Don't be silly," Josiah told her. "In the Yiddish version, the king sees the error of his ways and everyone is happy."

"If you think that's going to change Ma, you're crazy," Matilda told him.

"She's smart. She'll get the message," he predicted.

Matilda shook her head in disbelief.

He said, "You're all afraid of her. You'll see what happens when Naomi Nollman meets William Shakespeare."

The Friday evening after Max took Naomi to the theater, Lena was gloomy when she greeted Matilda and Josiah. "Ma won't come out of her room."

Josiah brightened. "What's the matter?"

Max, standing behind Lena, was smiling. "Since she saw *King Lear.*"

Susie and Sheldon arrived and were told about the situation. "Really?" Sheldon said. "What's she upset about?"

"She won't discuss it," Lena said.

"Why not?" Sheldon said.

Josiah was triumphant. He told Matilda, "I told you it would work."

Susie said, "What are you talking about?"

Josiah said, "Max took her to see the *Yiddish King Lear*. She got the message."

"What message?" Sheldon said.

Max laughed. "That we're tired of her coming and going whenever she feels like it."

Josiah said, "She knows who's the boss now."

Susie was doubtful. "That doesn't sound like Ma."

Josiah thought he knew better. "Shakespeare affects everyone. Even your mother."

Susie said, "If Ma met Shakespeare, he would be the one who would be affected. I'm going to talk with her."

She walked into Naomi's room and shut the door behind her. The others heard loud voices. There was silence. The door opened and Susie came out, looking thoughtful.

"What did she say?" Lena said.

"She's not coming out," Susie told them.

"Good," Josiah said.

Susie shook her head. "Until Josiah and Max apologize. She knows it was your idea," she said to Josiah.

"What?" Max said. "Never."

"Not until hell freezes over," Josiah said.

Max looked gloomy. Josiah implored him. "Don't give in."

Max said, "Easy for you to say. She's not in your bedroom."

Lena said to Max, "Okay, wise guy. What are we going to do?"

Matilda said, "I told you it wouldn't work."

Josiah shouted at her, "What do you mean? It worked. Look how upset she is."

Lena yelled at Matilda, "How could you let this happen?"

Matilda wept. "What could I do? Max took her to the theater, I didn't take her to the theater."

Sheldon laughed. "You're all nuts. You can't outguess her."

"I'm never going to apologize," Josiah said.

"Yes, you are," Matilda told him.

"The sooner the better," Susie told him.

Max stood. "I'm going to get it over with."

"Max, no," Josiah said.

They watched him vanish into the bedroom. He returned looking grim.

"So?" Josiah said. "What happened?"

"She's waiting for you," Max said.

Josiah paled.

"Get it over with," Matilda told him.

Josiah shook his head, a defeated man. He stood and vanished into the bedroom.

Sheldon said, "When is dinner?"

"As soon as the big shot comes out of the bedroom," Lena told him.

7. The Haberdasher

After high school, Charlie had found a job clerking part-time for Moe Fein in his leather goods store with a promise of a full-time position when one opened up. After a few years, Charlie thought about what it would be like to spend his life selling purses and hated the idea. Also, he knew that Fein's own sons had left the business because their father had a policy of never giving a raise, even to family.

Naomi talked to her sons-in-law. Times were bad, but Lena's husband, Max, knew someone who owed him a favor and had a job open for a traveling salesman of haberdashery.

Charlie complained to Max who was watching an older woman pin panels of muslin on one of his models. "Haberdashery! Am I a haberdasher? You think I'm going to sell ties and belts?" They were in Max's loft on Canal Street. Lightbulbs held by reflectors that dangled on long wires cast overlapping pools of light on the floor like spotlights on a stage. The floor-to-ceiling windows on the street side were grimy and interwoven with metal threads that translated even bright outside sunshine into an ineffective gray glow. Bolts of cloth stood like sentinels against the other three walls. The floor was littered with pieces of fabric. The model, a swaybacked blonde who looked about fifteen years old, was standing patiently while she was being draped.

"Not good enough for you, boychick?" Max was doing Charlie a favor and had no patience with him. He went to assist with the draping. "Like this, like this," he told the woman, taking the opportunity to pinch the model's bottom.

The draper knew Max from way back. "You want me to pinch her behind?" she said in a cigarette-husky voice. She turned to Charlie. "Ties and belts, and shirts, and underwear, and pajamas, and suspenders and handkerchiefs and socks."

"Oh, God," Charlie said.

"And also women's sewing notions." Thelma smiled.

"Thread, ribbons, thimbles and bobbins," Max said. "And thanks to keep your comments to yourself, Thelma," he said to the draper.

"What's a bobbin?" Charlie said gloomily.

"It goes on a sewing machine," Thelma said. "What's the route, Max?"

"The East Coast of Florida, all the way to Miami. It's a good route. Especially in the winter."

"My God," Charlie said.

Max was thinking about nights in small Southern towns. "Those girls climb all over Jewish boys from New York."

"And their brothers are right behind them with a shotgun." Thelma laughed. "We're going to miss you, Charlie."

"I don't want this job," Charlie said. "I've never been out of New York except to the Catskills. And I've never been away from the family."

"No, no. Let me, let me," Max said, approaching the model who eyed him warily. He moved some pins, rehung a panel, stepped back and said, "Now, see, I'm my own designer."

Charlie said, "I know I can't sleep on trains."

"How would you know?" Max had had enough of this conversation. "When did you ever?"

"I'm not a good sleeper."

"Max can sleep anywhere," Thelma said.

"Keep your comments to your own self, big mouth," Max told her.

Charlie was gloomy. "When do I start?"

"Monday." Max was approaching the model again. She looked to Thelma for help.

Thelma shrugged. "It's part of the job, honey."

Max walked around the model, shifting pins, pinching, feeling until the girl shivered.

"Hold still," he ordered.

"I can't help it," she whispered.

"Give Israel Roth my best," Max said to Charlie.

"Send us a postcard, Charlie," Thelma said.

"Hell," Charlie said.

8. Charlie's Decision

"What do you think, Matilda, should I take the job with Israel Roth?"

"Take it if you want to, Charlie."

"I'm not sure it's a good idea."

"Don't take it. Stay with Fein."

"I don't think I have a future with Fein."

"Go with Roth."

"I wish Fein liked me."

"Maybe Roth won't like you."

"He likes me. If he didn't, I wouldn't be talking about working for him."

"So what's the matter? Take the job."

"I'm trying to think long term. What makes the most sense for me? Maybe I shouldn't jump now."

"Charlie, don't bother me with your mishegoss. Go bother Lena."

"I'll make up my own mind."

"So why are you pestering me?"

"I just wanted to get your opinion."

"My opinion is take the job with Roth."

"I'm not sure it's the best job for me . . . in the long run."

"On the other hand, my opinion is you should jump out of the window- headfirst so you won't hurt yourself."

9. The Seaboard Line

Until he got his tickets at Pennsylvania Station, Charlie had never heard of the Seaboard Airline Railway. But the Seaboard line ran to the towns on Charlie's route. He and Lena sat at her kitchen table and pored over the railroad guide. "I'll be gone for three months," he told her, tracing his finger through stops in North Carolina: Raleigh, Southern Pines, Aberdeen, Pinehurst and Hamlet. "Look at these places. It's another world."

Lena was excited. "I wish I was going."

"I get my samples today. Israel Roth is going to take me through his line."

"Look," Lena said. "There's an Athens, Georgia."

"How can there be places with names like that? I can't believe this is happening to me."

"Watch out for those Southern belles." Lena jabbed his arm. "Oh, Charlie, dahlin'. Ah want to meet your whole family."

"Look at my stops in Florida. Look at this. I'm going to West Frostproof, Florida."

"What about Miami?"

"Miami is my last stop. Then I turn around and come home."

"Men are so lucky."

"I'd rather stay in New York," he said.

"I'd rather travel," she responded. "But I could never drag Max away from his models. Maybe you'll meet a nice girl, Charlie."

"I'm not that lucky," he said. "On the other hand," he thought, "Hey, you never know."

10. Pullman Follies

In the early evening outside of Penn Station, the huge columns lining the entrance seemed stately and welcoming, the stone eagles above the entry watched calmly as Charlie Nollman crossed the carriageway between honking cars and taxis. His two black travel cases with his samples and his one piece of personal luggage, a brown leather valise, a send-off gift from his sisters, were heavy, but he smiled at the redcaps and hung on to his burden. He went right through the arcade lined with shops and into the huge main waiting room with its honey-colored marble walls and pink marble floor and the vaulted ceiling towering above. He didn't stop until he was in the glass-roofed concourse above the tracks, with light flooding through the high windows and dust motes dancing in the sunbeams far above his head. He felt grand in his seersucker suit and spiffy new skimmer. He thought, *Oh, brother. I'm on my way.*

His deep reluctance to leave New York City and his family and his anxiety over having to travel for the first time throughout the South to sell his haberdashery were displaced by the excitement of his departure.

The train announcer's voice rang through the vast room. "Train number 165 with stops in Newark, New Jersey; North Philadelphia; Baltimore; Wilmington; Washington DC; and points south. All aboard."

"Points south. Oh, brother." Charlie descended the stairs to board the train. The platform was packed with passengers and friends, relatives and sweethearts saying goodbye, redcaps calling warnings as they pushed carts heavy with suitcases and trunks and conductors busily loading their gleaming train. "All aboard. All aboard."

Charlie boarded. A smiling porter approached and looked at his ticket. "Upper berth, sir," the man said. "I'm Franklin. Welcome aboard."

The seat facing Charlie was not yet occupied. The porter reached for the big sample cases. "These will have to be stowed in the rear of the car, sir. I'll bring you a claim check."

Charlie drew a deep breath and thought, *I wish the family could see this.* His eye was caught by a hubbub on the platform outside his window. An extremely fat man was using a cane to pry his way through the mob. He left a path wide enough so that a redcap had no problem following directly behind him with a baggage-filled cart. The fat man pointed his cane at Charlie's car and passed out of sight.

Charlie thought, *Uh oh.* Sure enough, the man entered the car and started down the aisle, checking seat numbers. He was perspiring and tapped a large handkerchief to his forehead. Charlie, who was nurturing a hope that a pretty young woman would sit across from him, prayed, "Not here, please."

The fat man put his suitcase on the seat across the aisle from Charlie. An older man, dignified in a tan suit and a green bow tie, wearing spats was in the opposite seat. He and Charlie watched the fat man sink down with a sigh, his bottom overlapping into the aisle.

Everyone's going to bump against him, Charlie thought.

The older man said, "How do you do." The fat man nodded and amused the older man by bouncing on his seat.

"You needn't make a face," the fat man said. "I have learned that I must make sure about the springs."

The older man nodded and pursed his lips as he pondered this unexpected information. The fat man, who was watching him closely, seemed satisfied with this response and smiled at Charlie who smiled back. The fat man studied his watch and announced that the train was scheduled to depart in five minutes.

The redcap, who had stowed the fat man's numerous cases in the baggage car, approached for his tip. The fat man dropped a wad of bills into his hand. The redcap looked at the bills in disbelief. The fat man explained to the older man and Charlie. "I believe in paying for services, don't you know?" He mopped his head. Perspiration was wetting the armpits of his jacket. He said, "Which way is the dining car, my man?"

The redcap said, "Don't you worry, boss. The conductor will announce when dinner is ready and which way is the dining car."

A pretty young woman entered the car and paused. She was blond, willowy and elegant in a broad-shouldered gray suit with a high slit in her long skirt and high-spiked heels like ones Charlie had seen stylish women wearing on Fifth and Madison Avenues. Around her slender white neck, she had draped two silver foxes and a long strand of pearls. *A rich shiksa*, he thought. *And gorgeous.*

The men in the car stared as she handed her ticket to the porter who led her down the aisle to the seat opposite Charlie.

Oh, brother, he thought. *Oh, brother.* He had never been close to this kind of woman who was clearly from a world far above the Lower East Side. He nodded to her, telling himself to be casual, but his excitement showed.

The young woman glanced at him. Her eyes were blue and penetrating. She stowed her personal baggage and furs in a storage compartment at the side of her seat, looked at the fat man, wrinkled her little nose, peered out the window at the thinning crowd on the platform and involved herself in a book.

A final "all aboard" from the conductors, a long whistle from the engine, the train began to glide, so smoothly that Charlie wasn't sure if his train was moving forward or the train on the adjacent track was moving backward.

"Oh, brother," he murmured. The young woman flicked her blue eyes at him and returned to the book. *Nothing new for her on this train*, he thought.

Everything was new to Charlie. He was steadily moving away from everything that he was comfortable with. He had lived his life in a Lower East Side tenement, surrounded by clamoring Jews and hustling Italians. To Charlie and his friends, the world outside of his neighborhood seemed difficult and confusing. "On the one hand, we all speak English," one of his sisters discussed their situation, "but on the other hand, who can understand these goyim? Do the same words mean the same thing? I don't think so."

The train was going faster. They were in a tunnel that Charlie knew ran under the Hudson River. When they emerged, there were water and reeds on both sides as far as he could see.

A conductor entered the car, a tall man, important in his uniform and cap. He announced in a tone that implied that this was his train and therefore everything that occurred from this point on would be with his permission, and that the next stop would be Newark, New Jersey, and that after the train departed Newark, dinner would be available in the dining car, three cars forward.

The fat man sighed with pleasure and bounced once.

The older man shook his head just a little and looked out the window when the fat man glanced at him.

There was a subtle adjustment in the speed of the train, an almost imperceptible slowing. Watery countryside gave way to farmland and clusters of shacks; laborers and children were waving to the train. Charlie waved back, feeling fine. The young woman did not look up.

Newark. Several passengers boarded. The train resumed its journey. Charlie heard chimes. A smiling porter at the end of the car was tapping a mallet on what looked like a small xylophone. The conductor announced that the dining car was open.

Charlie stood and stepped into the aisle. The fat man stood forcing, Charlie to sit again. Charlie looked at the young woman. Was she smiling? A little? He thought so.

The fat man had barely enough clearance to navigate between the seats. The older man rose. Charlie saw that he was nodding to himself, apparently bemused by the fat man's girth. He followed the fat man, and Charlie followed him. The young woman remained seated, reading her book.

Charlie was dazzled by the dining car. White linen tablecloths and napkins. Real silver utensils in a leather ring. Gold-trimmed china. Thin amber water goblets waiting to be filled. Fresh flowers in a slender crystal vase and a candle on each table. The headwaiter and the other waiters wore tuxedos. The chefs in white uniforms and tall white hats were visible in the galley through swinging latticed doors.

The dining car was already crowded. When the three men were seated, the fat man stuck out his big hand. "Waldo Pennington, sir."

The older man smiled. "I'm Henry Scoggins, my friends."

Charlie greeted them. "Charlie Nollman."

"The bill of fare, gentlemen." A waiter handed them sheets of paper and pencils. "Please check the items you wish to order."

Charlie looked at the paper and understood only one item, the price. Dinner would cost $2.25. Otherwise, he was baffled as he read the offerings: escargot; oysters Rockefeller; clams Casino; lobster salad à la russe; consommé a la canard; Dover sole with basil chiffonade; steak au poivre with julienne potatoes; boeuf bourguignon; polenta, sausage, and tomato en casserole; eggplant gruyere puree; Waldorf salad; ginger zabaglione with poached peaches; various flavors of ice cream.

The waiter appeared. "Have you decided, gentlemen?"

Charlie shook his head, pretending to study the menu.

"Do you mind, gentlemen?" It was the headwaiter. The young woman, Charlie's seat companion, was standing behind him. She was carrying her book. The older man, Scoggins, rose and bowed. "Of course not."

She smiled politely and examined the bill of fare.

The waiter returned. She was ready. "Escargot," she murmured as she checked items. "Consommé, the Waldorf salad, and the beef."

Pennington and Scoggins had no problem ordering. The waiter looked at Charlie. He had to choose something, so he noted the clams Casino, the steak au poivre and the eggplant puree. He had no idea what these were.

The waiter picked up their sheets and asked if they wanted setups for the table. Charlie looked at the other men. Scoggins said, "Yes, of course."

The waiter came back with glasses, small bottles of soda water and a bucket of ice cubes.

"I have a little something to add," Scoggins said and produced a slender flask from his inner pocket. Pennington and Charlie beamed. The young woman lifted her eyes and with no hesitation pushed forward her glass of ice cubes.

Scoggins poured from the flask and raised his glass to her. Charlie resisted the impulse to say, "L'chaim."

The young woman put down her book. Charlie could see the title. *An American Tragedy.*

Charlie read newspapers, especially the sports. He was a great fan of Grantland Rice, his favorite columnist in the *Journal American*. He picked up a magazine now and then. Books were of no interest.

Scoggins said, "How does this one compare with *Sister Carrie?*"

"They're very different," she told him. "I like it."

Pennington said, "I do so admire Dreiser."

She marked her page with a gold clip. "Pardon me," she said, "but we haven't been introduced. My name is Heather Sweetland."

Charlie had never heard anyone speak like Heather Sweetland. As she spoke, her lips barely moved. But the words, each one distinctly pronounced, tumbled lightly out of her small mouth. She did not sound anything like Charlie's sisters.

"I'm Charlie Nollman," he said, trying to match her modulated tone.

"Waldo Pennington," the fat man said.

"Henry Scoggins," the older man said. "You must be going to Palm Beach, Ms. Sweetland."

She sipped her drink and regarded him with interest. "Are you going there too, Mr. Scoggins?"

"Yes," he said casually. "I've been summoned by Mrs. Post. She wants me to escort a friend to the Red Cross Ball at the Mar-a-Lago."

Suddenly they were comfortable, like old friends. She smiled. "I imagine I'll see you there."

"I'm sure you will," he said. "I've known your mother, Elsie, for years."

Charlie, who had been feeling fine, was lost. He said to the fat man, "What about you? Aren't you going to Palm Beach?"

"No, indeed." Pennington said. "The Red Cross Ball is not for me." He waggled his massive shoulders. "I cause problems on the dance floor." He chuckled. It was more of a volcanic eruption than a laugh.

As the dinner progressed, Charlie, to his surprise, enjoyed the food. His companions, he thought, were sophisticated, at ease in a world he had perceived dimly and now wanted to be part of, if he could. Even Pennington, he realized, knew about the Red Cross Ball. Charlie thought about his Lower East Side family. The train was taking him far from that world. He drew a deep breath and settled back into his chair. He felt Heather appraising him and became uncomfortable. To divert her, he asked what *An American Tragedy* was about.

Heather, who had been rather reserved, as would have been expected sitting at dinner with three strange men, surprised them by leaning forward and putting her little hand on Charlie's. He blinked and resisted the temptation to put his free hand on hers. In a solemn voice, looking into his eyes, she warned him. "It is the story of a young man with a common background who wants to rise to the top."

Charlie sensed that in some manner he was about to be made fun of. But he couldn't help being interested in the book. "What happens?"

"The young man does rise," Heather said, "and he meets a wealthy young woman."

"Hey, why not?"

"Unfortunately, in order to win this wealthy woman he has to free himself of an attachment with another woman who is carrying his child."

"Wow."

"And he does this," she continued, "by doing away with the other woman. Actually, he drowns her in a lake."

"Oh, brother."

"He is caught by the police and ultimately executed." Heather sounded pleased by this act of justice.

"That's some book," Charlie said. "How do you know how it ends? You're only halfway through."

"A dear friend told me about it. He said that I must read it." She dazzled him with a smile and concluded, "It's a story of what can happen when somebody tries to rise out of his class."

Charlie felt like he was underwater.

As they ate their dessert, Scoggins told them about his career as an escort to society women in Palm Beach. "There is always competition for a suitable escort," he said. "My friends and I are reserved far in advance. One time, the day before an important ball, I received a phone call from the maid of my date. She was crying and told me that her mistress had just died. I was shocked. She had seemed to be in perfect health. An hour later, another woman, a friend of my late date, phoned me and said, 'I understand that you are available.'"

"Maybe there is hope for me as an escort," Pennington said. "Do you think that I would qualify?"

Scoggins smiled. "Let me know when you are in Palm Beach, Mr. Pennington."

Charlie asked Heather why she had stayed in the north while her family was already in Palm Beach.

Heather put down her fork and looked sad.

"What is it?" Charlie asked.

Heather's mouth trembled. "I don't know why I am telling you this."

"Okay," Charlie said, leaning forward in his chair.

She said softly, "I think that Mr. Scoggins will appreciate my dilemma . . ."

"Aha." Scoggins waved a hand at her and nodded.

She continued, "The man who recommended this book . . . he is a dear friend. Something occurred . . . that I did not foresee . . ." She appealed to Scoggins. "Do you understand?"

Scoggins was all encouragement. "Of course, my dear."

"I see," Charlie said; he did not see anything.

"Oh, dear," she said. "I could not permit him to think that I would . . . I am completely embarrassed. What must you all think?"

"You did what you had to do, my dear," Pennington said.

"You're all so kind. But I am embarrassed. I'm sorry. I must go."

They watched her walk rapidly out of the dining car.

So far, Charlie thought, he had risen successfully out of his class. Then he saw that Scoggins and Pennington were laughing.

Scoggins asked the fat man, "Do you think that in her haste, she failed to bring any cash?"

"My very thought," Pennington said.

"Shall we share her bill three ways?" Scoggins said.

Charlie understood at last. "Absolutely," he said. "How much do we tip?"

"Can I interest you in an after dinner drink?" Scoggins asked him as they were following Pennington out of the dining car. "I think you'll enjoy the lounge car."

They sat at a small table, sipping cognac. Charlie watched the older man swirl his brandy in the large glass and then sniff the fumes. He followed suit and coughed. Scoggins smiled and offered him a cigar. Charlie accepted and managed to light both of their cigars from one of the packs of matches resting on their ashtray. Scoggins stretched out his legs and moved casually in his chair so that his knee touched Charlie's. Accidentally? Charlie wondered. He broke the contact by shifting slightly to one side.

Scoggins, in a confidential voice, asked, "What did you think of Heather?"

Charlie swirled his brandy in his big glass and sipped. "What do you mean?"

"A sexy lady," the older man said.

"Yes," Charlie agreed with some feeling.

"Some men also enjoy the company of other men."

Charlie stared at him. "I don't."

Scoggins sipped his drink. "I thought not."

They drank, aware of each other, guarded. Charlie rose and said that he was going back to his berth. Scoggins, now rather wistful, said good night and that he might wait a bit and watch the lights of towns go by.

The Pullman car was transformed. Heavy green curtains screened the upper and lower berths. A short stepladder was waiting at the side of his berth. Charlie climbed and looked in. A small lamp showed that the bed was made up with two white sheets and a blanket. A pillow was set at the head. A towel, washcloth and a small bar of soap wrapped in paper were in the middle of the bed. His kit holding his razor, toothbrush and toothpaste was next to the towel. He thought, *this is really class.* He climbed down. There was no sound from the lower berth. "She's probably reading in bed," he thought.

He carried the towel and soap and his kit to the men's washroom. The basins were all occupied. Watching other men, Charlie realized that the lavatory had hot and cold running water. The faucets were gleaming brass. The sink was porcelain. Behind the sinks was a mirrored wall. He had never seen anything like it.

In his berth, Charlie turned off the light and looked out the small window.

Lights of a town were flashing by. Then darkness. He considered the rocking of
the train and the clacking sound of the rails. He thought about Heather. Was
she awake? Was there any way he could talk to her? Not that he could think
of. "Dumb," he told himself. He felt tired, but when he closed his eyes, he saw
Heather, the blanket pulled to her chin, sleeping soundly, the sleep of the rich.
He couldn't sleep. He concentrated on the sounds of the train, the whistle as
they sped through crossings, the clack, clack, clack of the wheels on the rails . . .
lights in his eyes from another town.

He slept until a book landed on his chest. For a moment he was baffled. He
turned on his light and saw that it was *An American Tragedy*. Heather had put
the book on his chest . . . in the middle of the night . . . in the dark . . . reaching
in through his curtain. Her gold clip marked a page of the book. A passage was
underlined. He read slowly, struggling to make sense of the passage; his heart
began to pound.

> The wonder and delight of a new and more intimate form of contact, of protest gainsaid,
> of scruples overcome! Days, when both, having struggled in vain against the greater
> intimacy which each knew that the other was desirous of yielding to, and eventually
> so yielding, looked forward to the approaching night with an eagerness which was as
> a fever embodying a fear. For with what qualms, what protests on the part of Roberta;
> what determination, yet not without a sense of evil, seduction, betrayal on the part of
> Clyde. Yet the thing once done, a wild convulsive pleasure motivating both.

"Oh, brother." He sighed. He decided to return the favor, reaching his arm
down to Heather's curtain and thrusting in the book. A hand grasped his wrist,
firmly. Checking to see if the aisle was empty, he followed his arm into her
berth. As he did, he saw the curtain across from him move slightly. *That was the
fat man. He saw me,* Charlie thought. *Oh, well.*

She greeted him with a passionate kiss and handed him a condom.

My God, he thought. *Oh, brother.*

As a teenager, Charlie had had his moments with neighborhood cuties.
With Heather Sweetland, he longed to play the role of sophisticated lover. But
he was uncertain. How, he wondered, does a man of the world make love to
such a woman?

After her torrid greeting, Heather had thrown her head back on the pillow
and closed her eyes. Clearly, she was waiting for him to begin. What should
he do first? Specifically, where should he touch her? Heather opened one eye.
"Well?" she said. "Are you paralyzed?" She closed her eyes and stirred her legs
under the cover.

Charlie thought about Mimi Schwartz who lived on the top floor of his
tenement and of their encounters on the stairs leading to the roof. If this were
Mimi Schwartz, he thought, she would have grabbed his balls and reeled him
in, laughing like a hyena. But this was Heather Sweetland, another creature

from another country. Charlie put a tentative hand on one of her legs. Heather reached up, grabbed his balls and giggled. From this point on, Charlie was in familiar territory.

In the late night, before she dismissed him, thinking about the condom, he said, "You were ready for everything."

She nodded and explained the obvious. "I wouldn't want to have a Jewish baby. Good night."

Back in his berth, Charlie was upset. What had happened, he thought, was not a conquest. He had not impressed Heather Sweetland. In fact, in a flash of awareness, Charlie realized that he had been used. For a moment, he considered returning to Heather's berth and dominating her with his Jewish masculinity. But he knew that this was a foolish idea. Anyway, he told himself, he had one hell of a story to tell his friends in New York.

11. Fat Man in a Hot Southern Town

In his skimmer and his seersucker suit, Charlie crossed the street in Deluxe, Georgia, on his way to Mendelsohn's Dry Goods Emporium. He lifted his feet carefully because the asphalt was already soft in the late morning sun, and if you weren't watchful it could shift from your shoes to your pants cuffs.

Because the noon sun pretty well shuts things down until about three o'clock, Charlie was in the store at 11:00 a.m. to meet with Hy Mendelsohn, a thin, bald, cheerful, energetic, small-town Jewish merchant of whose type Charlie came to recognize as smiley and narrow-minded. Who should clump in, filling the whole doorway, but Pennington, the fat man from the train. The people on the street were staring at him through the store window. Charlie said, "Hello, I know that fellow."

That he and Pennington were in town on this particular midsummer morning was a coincidence. After disembarking in Athens, Georgia, an important stop on the Seaboard Airway Railroad Line, Charlie had scheduled a day in Deluxe in order to flog his line of notions. Two months ago, he had only a small idea of what haberdashery was. Now he was lugging two big black cases filled with samples: zippers; pins (straight and safety, various sizes); thread (seven colors) wound on large and medium-sized wooden spools; thimbles (wrought iron, zinc and porcelain); handkerchiefs (frilly and useful); lace (white and beige) for cuffs and collars; bobbins; artificial flowers (a big seller); other small chachkes; and a last-minute addition, birthday and anniversary cards. Charlie's boss, Israel Roth, had said, "Why not? Give them a try."

Charlie had just pulled out a card of zippers when the overweight gentleman advanced into the store, held out his hand to Hy and said, "Edgar Pennington."

Hy grabbed as much of the hand as he could, while using both of his hands.

Pennington turned to Charlie with a big smile and said, "Hello there, traveling companion. Fancy meeting you here. What are you doing in this fine little Southern town?"

"Business," Charlie told him. "And what brings you to Deluxe?"

Hy answered for Pennington. "The Deluxe Sanitarium."

"Indeed, yes," Pennington said.

"It's famous," Hy said.

"Yes, it is, it is," Pennington agreed. "Known throughout the land as the place to come to for people who want to drop a few pounds and more than a few dollars."

Hy knew the drill: "And you're in my place to buy clothes that are three or four sizes smaller than the ones you're wearing."

"They think that will motivate me." Pennington laughed. "Actually, I'll probably donate them back to you, sir."

Hy smiled. "You won't be the first one. Excuse me, Nollman," he said and proceeded to wait on Pennington. Charlie sat on a chair next to the cash register and picked up a copy of *Colliers*. This proved to be fateful. When Pennington was done buying the clothes, he came over to the cash register and looked down at the *Colliers*. Next thing Charlie knew, Pennington said, "Excuse me, do you mind?" He grabbed the magazine and said, "Look at this. Look at this." He showed Charlie a picture of an airplane.

Hy came over to see what the fuss was about. Pennington waved the magazine at him. "It's the new Stout airplane, the Maiden Detroit," he said. "And I have bought one. They're flying it right to Deluxe. To your own little airport," he explained to Hy. "So I don't have to take the train home," he said to Charlie.

Pennington was running on about the Maiden Detroit. "It's entirely metal," he told Hy. "It can carry eight passengers. And it's got a new Liberty engine."

Charlie and Hy stared at each other and at Pennington. Hold on there! The man had bought an airplane! How could one person buy a big airplane! And have it flown to Deluxe! What were we dealing with here!

What they were dealing with, they realized, was a fat rich man, a very fat, very rich man.

And Hy was saying silly things like, "Let me show you my line of straw hats." As if Pennington needed a hat. He undoubtedly had a hundred hats. And Charlie realized that Pennington was not likely to be interested in notions. So he had nothing to sell him. "What about a gross of linen handkerchiefs, Mr. Pennington?"

"Well," Pennington said, "I guess I'll be going along. They'll be serving my so-called lunch in a bit." He shook his head, his jowls lagging behind his chin; it looked strange. He smiled at Charlie. "Well, sir, it has been a pleasure to see you again."

"It certainly has," Charlie told him.

Pennington took a few steps toward the door and turned. "Unless you would care to join me for lunch."

Charlie was surprised and didn't know what to say. Lunch did not seem like a good idea; what would they serve at the Deluxe Sanitarium?

Pennington nodded. "Lunch is no treat, but you might enjoy a ride in my new Dusenberg touring car."

"Dusenberg?" Charlie murmured.

"Touring car?" Hy sighed.

"It's a grand ride," Pennington said. "And the local folks get a kick out of my chauffeur, don't you know?"

"Aha," Charlie said. "Your chauffeur."

"Yes," Pennington said. "Galsworthy. He's from England. He drove the car down from New York."

Charlie took a deep breath. "Mr. Pennington, I would be happy to ride with you and Galsworthy. Will you watch my sample cases, Hy?"

They emerged into the August glare and stopped to catch their breath. Pennington panted. "This heat is too much for me."

The heat in Deluxe was not like New York City heat. In New York, a heat wave could shut you down. Walk the hot sidewalks, and the heat transferred through the soles of your shoes to your feet and up through your body to meet, somewhere in the middle of your chest, the humid temperature that was descending from your stewed brains even though you were wearing a straw hat.

Charlie had discovered that in the South there were no heat waves. The whole summer was a continual unrelenting swelter. In late May, the daytime temperature ratcheted up and then stayed in the mid to high nineties until October.

Georgians knew how to deal with it. They took shallow breaths. They talked slowly. They never rushed; they strolled from house to auto to store or office. By the time Charlie reached Deluxe, he had learned to slow down. Toting his sample cases down Main Street, he understood the men who sat in front of the stores, tilting back, straw hats pulled almost over their eyes, smoking cigarettes and pipes, Coke bottles in hand and relaxing into their drawling conversations. *I could be happy here, for a while*, Charlie thought.

Pennington's Dusenberg was a tan roadster and high off the ground. A person had to step on the running board and then take one more step up into the car. From cream-colored leather seats, the passengers looked down at folks on the sidewalk.

Galsworthy, a thin little man, sat behind the wheel wearing goggles, a touring cap and suede gloves. He had paid a local young fellow in blue coveralls to wield the crank. The engine started with a crash and a backfire. Galsworthy squeezed a rubber ball mounted on his side of the car. The horn went *auooga, auooga*. He worked with the gearshift, and the car began to roll down Main Street followed by a happy parade of shouting boys and barking dogs.

"'Ere we go, gents," Galsworthy crowed.

Pennington was proud. He yelled into Charlie's ear, "How do you like my Doozy?"

How did he like it? Charlie loved it. He held onto his skimmer and laughed out loud as the Doozy rolled down the street attracting the rapt attention of gentlemen and ladies who waved at the two smiling men in the rear seat and at Galsworthy who tootled his horn at everyone in sight.

The road led into the countryside. Cows dotted the landscape; clustered under the few trees, their legs folded under them to save energy. They swung their heads at the car. Galsworthy blew his horn. Pennington shouted, "Moooo!" The cows munched thoughtfully, perhaps mistaking him as one of their own, Charlie thought, then reprimanded himself for being unkind to his host.

Pennington was, in fact, of two minds about losing weight. He rather enjoyed being a battleship in a world of rowboats and canoes. Nevertheless, to placate his doctor and a semi-hysterical mother, he had reluctantly enrolled himself in the Deluxe Sanitarium.

The car turned into a road that led up a hill to a building that looked liked an old castle with towers. There was a moat that had to be crossed by a drawbridge. Galsworthy squeezed the bulb of his horn—*auooga*—and drove up to the entrance of the building. Two men dressed in metal chain-link jackets and carrying lances and shields greeted them. The men raised their lances in a salute as Pennington pushed himself out of the car and said to Charlie, "Wait'll you catch this show."

They passed through a corridor that featured suits of armor tucked into alcoves, turned a corner and were in the dining room, a cavernous space adorned with flags and pennants. Large people sat expectantly on benches at long tables. In a corner, seated in front of an enormous tapestry that displayed stags, hunting dogs and knights on horseback, a small band was playing a tinkly tune on harps and other stringed instruments that Charlie recognized as "Dixie."

Waiters wearing tasseled caps and purple capes passed among the diners carrying trays of cottage cheese and melba toast. Bowls of fresh fruit waited on the tables along with pitchers of water. A man wearing a full suit of armor, including a metal helmet emblazoned with a coat of arms, approached Pennington. He opened his visor and said, "Ah, we feared you were going to miss luncheon, Mr. Pennington."

"Not for the world, Mr. Merlin," Pennington said. He gestured to Charlie. "This is my friend, Mr. Nollman."

Mr. Merlin beamed. "I am so pleased to meet you, Mr. Nollman. My name is Merlin, Arthur Merlin. I'm the director of this sanitarium. I hope you are joining us for luncheon, though I'm afraid it is poor fare for a man with a hearty appetite."

"Not at all," Charlie said. "I'm happy to join you and your guests." He turned to Pennington. "Is that his real name?"

"Who knows," Pennington replied. "At times I wonder if this whole place is real."

Pennington and Charlie took their places at the table. Mr. Merlin clanked into the space next to Charlie and asked what he was doing in Deluxe. Charlie explained his sales mission. "The dollar is the Holy Grail, is it not?" Merlin sighed. Charlie agreed and ladled himself a large ball of cottage cheese.

Pennington filled his plate with a tower of cottage cheese, then cut up three apples and three oranges that he piled on his cottage cheese and added sliced watermelon, cantaloupe, peaches, plums, dates, figs and cashews. He sighed, bent over his plate, and sucked up the contents in a prolonged whoosh.

"That's how fat people swallow their food," Merlin murmured to Charlie. To Pennington, he said, "You must learn to eat more slowly, Mr. Pennington."

"I was eating slowly, Mr. Merlin," Pennington told him.

The harpist and the other musicians swung into a tinny rendition of "Alexander's Ragtime Band."

Waiters passed out bowls of rice pudding. Pennington swallowed his pudding in a gulp. Charlie, who hated rice pudding, passed his to Pennington who nodded gratefully and sucked it in, barely avoiding the spoon that Charlie had left embedded in the pudding.

Pennington turned to Charlie and said, "Watch this." He was looking at the entrance to the hall where a man dressed in green trousers and a brown jacket appeared with a horn about six feet long. He blew a blast. The diners applauded. He blew again and again, the sound reverberating against the walls of the big hall.

Mr. Merlin rose and waved his arms, then removed his helmet. "I can't really make myself heard with this thing on. Where is Friar Tuck?" he said.

A stout, smiling round-faced man wearing a floor-length tan robe and a little brown skullcap over his shaved spot on his head approached and handed a scrap of paper to Mr. Merlin who said, "There you are."

He studied the paper. "Here is the winner." The diners leaned forward. Mr. Merlin called out numbers. "Four, two, seven, three." He looked around. Nobody stirred. "Come, come, people," he said. "Who is the lucky winner?"

There was a chuckle next to Charlie. Pennington rose and waved a ticket.

"Well, bless me," he said. "I never win these things, and I seem to have won the lottery."

Mr. Merlin examined the paper. "You have, sir. You have indeed."

Pennington made a mewing sound.

"All right," Mr. Merlin called out. "Everybody to the moat."

Charlie hadn't looked closely at the moat when they entered the castle, but now had his chance as he followed a clanking Mr. Merlin and group of retainers, all of whom had recently staffed the dining room. The men were dressed now as squires carrying shields, and the women as ladies-in-waiting in tall peaked caps with wafting veils. The entourage walked slowly down a winding staircase to the boat landing.

"Whoa," Charlie said. "Sharks!"

This observation caused considerable merriment among Mr. Merlin and his crew.

"Look again, sir," Mr. Merlin cackled. "The sharks you see floating around in the moat are in fact made of rubber."

Charlie looked and saw that the sharks were bobbing harmlessly. "Could have fooled me," he said. Then one of the fake sharks suddenly vanished with a sucking sound from the surface of the moat.

"What was that?" Charlie asked.

"Hmm," Mr. Merlin said. Turning to a young boy dressed as a page, he said, "I thought we had gotten rid of that alligator."

"We haven't figured out how to do that, sir," the boy replied.

Mr. Merlin shook his head. "I have to do everything myself." Then he said to Charlie, "Ten years ago, one of the group played a small prank and slipped a baby alligator into the moat."

"It grew," Charlie understood.

"Tremendously," Mr. Merlin affirmed. "On the positive side," he continued, "we have had no problems in the castle with vermin, or with cats or dogs." He then looked at the moat and said, "But here comes your yacht, Mr. Pennington, for your trip around the moat."

The "yacht" was actually a rowboat propelled by none other than Friar Tuck who had doffed his clerical robes in favor of a more nautical outfit adapted from a U.S. Navy sailor's uniform. The friar was smiling and waving when the alligator, which had turned upside down, floated by the boat with his belly up. The good friar interpreted this position as a taunt and smacked the alligator's belly with his oar. The alligator flipped over and pummeled the boat with his powerful tail. The friar roared in anger and beat on the alligator with his other oar.

"No no, my dear friar," Mr. Merlin shouted. "You are going to harm our Albert."

There were contradictory versions by Mr. Merlin and his staff about what happened next. This much was agreed on. Friar Tuck, enraged and hopping about in the boat, lost his balance and fell overboard. Albert proceeded to chomp on the friar who let out a piercing bellow. The alligator, in turn, emitted a loud reptilian groan and plunged into the depths of the moat.

The friar, undamaged though slightly scratched and considerably shaken, was hurriedly pulled from the moat.

"I believe I will pass on the cruise," Pennington said.

"What in God's name happened?" Charlie asked.

Mr. Merlin knew. "Albert," he explained as if it were the most natural thing in the world, "has a serious dental problem."

"Really?" Charlie said.

"In fact," Mr. Merlin said, "he suffers from excruciatingly sensitive gums."

"Poor creature," Charlie said.

"Exactly," Mr. Merlin agreed and added, "we've known about this condition for some time and have had to slice its raw fish into bite-sized pieces. The creature should never have attempted to chomp the friar."

Charlie considered the moat, the friar, the rowboat and the unfortunate Albert. He could not wait to write about this whole episode to his family in New York. He shook his head and said, "This would never have happened on the Lower East Side."

"It should not have happened in Georgia either," Pennington said. "In fact, I believe that it is time to leave this establishment." He started back up the path to the sanitarium, followed by Charlie, an apologetic Mr. Merlin, a chastened Friar Tuck and the rest of the entourage.

The Deluxe airport consisted of a shack, a wind sock and a long strip of mowed grass. The Stout airplane had made several passes over the field until the pilot was satisfied that he was in the right place, with Pennington and Charlie waving frantically, and deftly deposited the plane on the turf runway.

Pennington said to Charlie, "Are you sure you want to go to Miami, Mr. Nollman?"

Charlie's suitcase and sample cases were waiting next to the runway. "Absolutely, I have a reservation at the Roney Plaza Hotel in Miami Beach. Why don't you join me, Mr. Pennington?"

Pennington declined. "In fact, Mr. Nollman, I'm flying my plane on to Key West. I hear there is another sanitarium there."

"What about the Doozy?" Charlie asked.

"Galsworthy will meet me in Key West," Pennington told him.

"Sounds like a good plan," Charlie said.

Part Four:
A Match Made in Heaven

1. At the Roney

"Ma, Flo Jacobs wants me to go to Miami Beach with her . . . She's going to pay for the whole thing . . . Her husband will only let her go if she has a companion . . . You like her, don't you, Ma? . . . Please, Ma, Miami Beach . . . I'll die if I miss this chance . . . Miami Beach. Oh, God, . . . you can't say, no, Ma."

Poolside at the Roney Plaza, Ida studied herself in her black bathing suit, her long black hair piled into her white bathing cap, her face, neck, shoulders, arms and legs covered with Coppertone. She wanted to go home as tan as an Indian, but Flo had warned her about the Miami Beach sun. Feeling fine, she hadn't yet gone into the pool. She hugged her knees and splashed the water. She actually laughed out loud.

"Say, you look like you're enjoying yourself."

Ida looked up into the Miami Beach sun, shaded her eyes with her hand and saw a slender young man wearing a dark green one-piece bathing suit. He was standing next to her and smiling. She looked down at the water and did not respond, but he saw the quick expression of pleasure that she could not contain.

"Mind if I try that?" He didn't wait for an answer, sat next to her and began to splash his feet alongside of hers. She edged away, but not far.

He inched closer. "I haven't seen you here before. Did you just arrive or are you somebody's guest?"

Her heart was pounding. She frowned and looked at the water, at the lifeguard, at other bathers, anywhere but at him.

"My name is Charlie Nollman. Unless you're taken. Are you taken? It's no use not talking to me. I want to get to know you."

Ida glanced at him. She murmured without conviction, "What a nerve."

"Have you ever been on an ocean cruise?"

She arched her penciled eyebrows. "Who wants to know?" She felt so awkward. She hated feeling awkward; her own voice sounded strange to her. What a silly thing to say. She was afraid he was seeing through her pretense at sophistication.

But he said, "You're so pretty. Look, I'm not some kind of gigolo. But the Roney is like a ship on the ocean. Everybody is here for a good time, everybody meets other people."

His tone was so friendly, so earnest, so respectful, she knew he had to be okay. Still without looking at him, she said, "I'm here with a companion."

"Oh, oh," he said, disappointment in his voice. "Sorry. You're sitting here all by yourself. I thought, well . . ."

"A female companion," she said, liking his reaction.

"Aha," he said, revived. "And where is this companion?"

"In our room, calling a friend on the telephone. She'll be here in a few minutes."

"Well, that's nice. Why don't we splash again so she'll see us?"

He began to splash and she joined in, laughing. They sent up a geyser of water. People near them moved away, and that made them laugh louder. Ida loved being at this pool, at this hotel, in Miami Beach and playing with a nice-looking young man she didn't even know. It was so far from cold Detroit. It was what she had imagined. She felt superior to the people at home living a dingy life, Ma, Pa, Sarah.

"So what's your name?" Charlie said.

"Ida."

"Ida?"

"Ida Haberman."

"Ida?" The voice was behind them. It was Flo wearing a flowered sundress, sandals, a big yellow straw hat and yellow-framed sunglasses.

Ida and Charlie jumped up. She was a little flustered, Charlie was grinning. He stuck out his hand to Flo. "I'm Charlie Nollman."

Flo was not interested. "How do you do, Mr. Nollman? You'll have to pardon us. Ida, there's somebody I want you to meet."

"Hey." He was left with his hands on his hips. Ida looked back and shrugged; there was time. She liked being hard to get. Lots of fish in the ocean, she thought.

Flo led her to a cabana and a big man sitting in a canvas lounge chair, smoking a cigar with a fizzy drink loaded with lemons, oranges and pineapple, a whole fruit salad in a glass, on the little table next to him. He had a heavy face, thick lips, a fleshy nose. The top of his brown-striped bathing suit was parted from the bottom by his paunchy stomach. Curls of black hair stuck out around his top, up his neck, down his shoulders and above his trunks. His legs were covered with hair. Ida's father was almost hairless. Charlie Nollman, still standing at the pool and watching—she had glanced back at him—had hair under his arms and a little mustache. This man, she thought nervously, was like a gorilla.

"This is Ken Ross," Flo said. "Ken has invited us to go for a ride in his car."

Ross appraised Ida who felt like squirming, but didn't. He nodded to Flo. "Okay, let's go."

His car was a light green four-door Packard roadster with a white cloth top that folded back, white-walled tires, a rack in the back for luggage, and, Ken showed them, twin windshields that folded down.

"What a car," Flo said.

"You know who rode in this car," he told them as they mounted the running board and got into big Packard. "Lindberg rode in this car, that's who. In a parade."

Ida, wearing a terrycloth robe over her bathing suit, was in the backseat "where Lindberg sat." Flo wedged herself against Ken. This was the arrangement for the next week; they were a threesome, making day trips up and down the coast, to Palm Beach to look at the big houses, down to Key Biscayne, stopping at terrific little places for lunch and back to the Roney for dinner, with Ken pretending that he wasn't holding Flo's hand under the tablecloth, and Flo looking entirely satisfied.

Who were they kidding? Ida played along.

Nights they would stay at the hotel bar drinking, and Ida, tipsy, would say good night and go to their room. If she woke up when Flo rolled in, she would say nothing while Flo undressed in the bathroom.

One night in the Roney's big dining room, she caught sight of Charlie Nollman. He was seated with three gorgeous girls and laughing a lot. He waved to her. She waved back, a stiff wave. Flo saw the exchange and laughed. Ida blushed. She knew why she was there. That was the bargain. People like Flo and Ken Ross took what they wanted and didn't care. That's what Ida learned on this trip.

When Ken was out fishing for tarpon, Ida and Flo had lunch in a restaurant looking out at Biscayne Bay. Ida said, "How long have you known him?"

Flo smiled. "We met last year. Are you having a good time?"

"Sure." *Good time? Well, maybe I'm getting more than I bargained for. How can I get them to stop bringing me along?*

"Thank you for coming." Flo was studying a menu. "Detroit is so cold now. And all that snow. Maybe we can do this again next winter."

Ida nodded and said nothing.

Flo looked at her. "Something wrong?"

Ida smiled. "Of course not, not when I think about Detroit."

Flo looked at her sharply. "Nice hotels here, nice restaurants, clubs."

"A long way from Detroit," Ida said.

"Maybe we'll leave you at the Roney from now on. Would you mind that?"

"I think that would be a good idea."

Flo could see that Ida meant it. She relaxed. "Wait until your family sees you with that tan. And I think we're all putting on a few pounds."

There were two weeks left before they had to go home. Flo told Ida that she and Ken were going off by themselves. "He wants his privacy. And he's going to be meeting some people on business. You'll be better off here."

"Fine," Ida said. "Fine."

"You behave yourself," Flo said. "And don't get involved with that Charlie. I promised your mother to take good care of you."

At the poolside the next day, Charlie found Ida sitting by herself in a canvas lounge chair sipping an iced tea. "Ken Ross!" He laughed. He had an infectious, high-pitched laugh that Ida liked. "You mean Ken Rosenberg. He's my cousin. What a character. What a car. Big bucks. He has connections with some New York mob people. Maybe Meyer Lansky. He's here, too. You almost never see him. He's a little guy, only five feet tall, in that cabana over there that you can't see into. Just don't call him sunny boy. And anyway, what about us?"

"Mr. Ross says he's a builder," Ida said, ignoring his question.

"Sure, and I'm King George. Are you free for dinner? There's a great place. Joe's Stone Crabs. Have you ever eaten stone crabs? I'll show you how. Ida, I'm so glad you're back. We're going to have a terrific time."

Flo telephoned once. "We're in Key West. Are you behaving yourself? You better. We'll be back in a week. He wants to go to Cuba."

Dressing in her room, Ida felt like she was dreaming. *Am I pretty? Is this dress flattering? Ida couldn't make up her mind. What about Charlie? He likes me. He must have money. He wanted me to open my mouth when he kissed me. He knows things. It's not like home. Would Ma like him? He's a good dancer. Flo doesn't care. She just wants to be with that Ken. Both of them are married, and they don't care. Charlie, are you going to want to do it? Should I let him? I know he wants to. Ma, what should I do?*

"Where have you been?"

"Am I late, Charlie?"

"You're a half hour late. I thought you must have met somebody else."

Ida laughed. "Where are we going?"

"To the Delmonico. We have reservations."

"Charlie! Wow!"

Last night alone. In Ida's room. Flo and Ken were due the next day.

"Charlie, you shouldn't be in here."

"It's okay. We're going together, aren't we?"

"We don't really know each other, Charlie."

"What are you talking about? Come here."

"Oh . . . Charlie . . . don't."

"Why not? Hold still. What's the matter?"

"I can't. I promised."

"What? Who? Not Flo, for Pete's sake. And what are you worried about? I'm going to marry you."

"Charlie!"

"Sure. Why not? Come here."

"Charlie . . ."

"What? Ida, what?"

"I want to wait."

"Oh, brother." He reached out and reeled her in like she was a sailfish on the hook.

They were in bed when the overhead light was switched on. Flo was staring at them.

Ida hid her face in the pillow. Charlie glared at Flo. "We didn't expect you."

Flo was grim. "We came back early. Please leave us, Mr. Nollman."

Charlie shrugged and swung out of bed. He pulled on his pants, patted Ida's hip and strolled to the door. "See you later, honey."

Flo shook her head. "Ida, I hope you took precautions."

"It doesn't matter," Ida told her. "We're going to get married."

"You are really a stupid girl," Flo said.

Ida sat up, covering herself with the sheet. "No, I'm not," she said. "Anyway, I had a good teacher, didn't I?"

She didn't tell Flo that she had arrived in the nick of time before it had actually happened.

2. Married

Rabbi Baruch Ginsberg pulled his tollis over his shoulders, opened his prayer book and cleared his throat. He looked at the couple standing before him. The young man was nicely dressed in a three-piece gray suit, flowered tie, white handkerchief peeping from his breast pocket and gray spats over his black shoes. He was frowning and biting his lip, nervously pushing at the tip of his long nose. The young woman wore an ankle-length black silk dress, a string of pearls and a dark green cloche over curly black hair cut short in the flapper style. A white orchid corsage, no longer perky, drooped from the collar of her dress.

Noting that the young woman seemed distracted, Rabbi Ginsberg cleared his throat again and began to recite a blessing: "Baruch atah Adonai . . ."

Ida wasn't listening. How had this happened? She had always dreamed of a big wedding with a band, deluxe food and champagne. She would dance with her new husband until all hours, cut the tiered cake and listen to humorous and ribald toasts by their friends and families. Then afterward, in their hotel room, her husband would sweep her off her feet, carrying her along with his passion, overcoming her fear. And the next day, on a train in a private compartment, they would go to Niagara Falls with matching luggage filled with her trousseau and her husband's suits, both of them packing sporty clothes and sturdy shoes for walking arm in arm, her lacy nightgown and wonderful nights . . . and champagne toasts . . . and sighing . . . heads together . . . sharing thoughts, desires . . . he would understand her . . . her shyness . . . her sensitive nature . . . he would protect, honor and cherish . . . the rabbi's words . . .

"Do you, Chaim Nollman . . . ?"

Charlie was worried. Would this be enough for her? She was so young.

She had told him about her fantasies of a big wedding. In Florida, she had thought he was a big shot. He was such a spiffy dresser, a big spender on money borrowed from his brother-in-law, Sheldon Bergstresser, who would never miss it. How could she know? But times were bad, and he was out of work. He had told her that he loved her, but that he had to conserve money. He told her not to worry, he would always do all right, and they would be happy . . . and he had enough for a week in Niagara Falls, even though it was November, thanks to a loan from Lena and Max who had to come up with the money. "Either that or I'll make it on the street," she told Max and he wasn't sure that she was bluffing; he knew she'd do anything for her darling brother.

"Do you, Ida," a quick glance at his notes, "Haberman . . . ?"

The wedding party consisted of her mother, father and sister, Sarah, in their good clothes standing stiffly, along with Lena and Max, the maid of honor and the best man, "all the way from New York City," Charlie kept saying. Afterward, they would go to Boesky's restaurant on Twelfth Street, not exactly the ballroom of the new Book Cadillac Hotel.

Could he make her happy? She wanted to live in Detroit near her parents. Maybe they had a little money . . . maybe they would help him get started. Detroit . . . away from his family . . . how could he do that? His whole life he had been near his family. Was he making a big mistake? Too late. Too late.

Max was handing him the ring.

"I now pronounce you . . . That's fifteen dollars, mister . . . thank you and mazeltov."

Max produced a flask and some shot glasses. The rabbi beamed. "L'chaim," they all toasted. Charlie had two shots. Ida choking on her drink, finally swallowed a few drops. Charlie clinked glasses with Lena who sang "By Meir Bist Du Schein," which she loved to sing, and then launched into "My Yiddisha Mama," even though it was a little sad for the occasion.

Charlie realized that his sister was drunk and said, "Thanks for the songs. We gotta get to the restaurant."

"*Shuffle off to Buffalo,*" Lena sang.

Max grabbed the flask before the rabbi could pour himself another shot. "At least you know what to do tonight," he told Charlie.

Ida didn't like the way Charlie laughed.

3. Niagara Falls

First time. It hurt. Ida bled, to her surprise and dismay. She didn't know that that was what happened; she told Charlie who was upset that she was upset.

First day. Breakfast in bed. Charlie buttered and sliced her toast and fed it to her, square by square. "Open up now, little sweetie," he said, and she laughed and did as he told her. Now this was fun, at last.

Charlie said it was time to see the falls and started looking at his casual suits in the closet. He was a dresser, choosing his suit carefully. She felt her heart begin to beat. "Charlie . . ."

He looked at her and saw that she was worried about something.

"What's the matter, sweetie?"

"What do you think the women are wearing?"

What was this about? "Why? What's the difference?"

"I want to look right, Charlie. I don't know if this is a dressy place or not."

He sat next to her on the bed and took her hand. "Nobody is going to look as pretty as you, Ida."

She sighed. "Charlie . . ." He didn't know exactly what was on her mind until she told him that she wanted him to go downstairs so that he could report on how the young women were dressed.

Charlie was a good sport and did it for her. "Casual," he told her. "Sweaters and skirts and no hats. Ankle stockings. White."

She was satisfied. So was he. He didn't know that for the rest of their married lives, she would never leave her hotel room on the first morning until he checked on the fashion.

4. Twins

Ida did not admit that she was pregnant until she was in her fifth month, and the family and her gang could hardly miss her enlarged breasts and the bulge in her abdomen. She had stopped being sick to her stomach in the mornings, thank God, but hated what was happening to her body. She tried on dress after dress.

"When are you going to wear maternity clothes?" Charlie said.

"I don't need them yet. This looks okay, doesn't it?"

Charlie, who was always well dressed with his trimmed mustache and manicured fingernails, did not know how Ida could look in the mirror and not see that her long, close-fitting gray silk emphasized the changes in her figure. "It's fine." He saw no point in making her even more unhappy.

Within a month, Ida couldn't get into that dress. Dr. Leo Birnbaum, listening to heartbeats with his stethoscope, told her why. "Twins. You're having twins. I can hear two heartbeats. Do you want to hear them?"

"No." She began to sniffle.

Dr. Birnbaum patted her hand. "It'll be fine. Two for the price of one. A double joy."

"I don't want twins."

Dr. Birnbaum did not like unhappy patients. A big man, unassailable in his long white coat, his thick brown mustache bulky under a bulbous nose, he was dedicated to his patients and insisted, in turn, on nothing less than total trust and gratitude. But he knew pregnant women and sensed that he was at an impasse with Ida. She was a whiner and was demanding something from him other than what he normally delivered: her girlish figure and something more that the doctor could not be bothered with, her girlish daydreams.

"Well, Ida dear," he said, doing his best to be soothing, "that's what Mother Nature has given you. I'll bet you can't wait to tell Charlie."

Ida looked at her large belly. Her distaste grew when she pictured herself wheeling one of those double buggies taking up the whole sidewalk. "There are no twins in my family," she said. "They must be from his side."

"I want you to come in every two weeks," he told her. "I want to follow you closely."

Ida hated him. "Why? I'm all right, aren't I?"

"Absolutely. But we don't want any surprises."

"You've already given me my surprise." She pulled the sheet up to her neck. "I have to leave. I have a game. The girls will be waiting."

When Ida was dressed and leaving the office, the nurse, who was pretty in her white uniform and slender as a twig, made a notation in her appointment book and called out, "He wants you to come back in two weeks, Mrs. Nollman. Is two o'clock on Wednesday good for you?"

Ida was the best bridge player in her crowd. Eleanor, her close friend, had no card sense. The others put up with her because what else could they do? Mildred and Irene had read Culbertson and had some understanding of the game, but they did not count cards; Mildred because she just couldn't, Irene because she wouldn't take it seriously enough to make the effort. The group met twice a week in the afternoons and enjoyed the talk and the nibbles. After they had lit their cigarettes and smoke began to layer the room, Eleanor said, as she was shuffling the cards, "Well, what did Dr. Birnbaum say?"

Ida had told them about her appointment. Eleanor was interweaving the cards then bending the deck so that it would flutter together. Ida did not reply. Her friends knew that if she were unhappy about something, she would not want to discuss it. So heads cocked inquisitively.

Ida ignored them. Mildred, who was pleased when somebody had a problem, said eagerly, "You look like you have something on your mind, Ida. Come on, you're among friends."

Ida drew deeply on her cigarette and emitted a long stream of smoke. She said to Eleanor, "Aren't you going to deal? You're shuffling the spots off the cards."

Eleanor was sensitive to criticism, real or perceived, especially when it was delivered by Ida, the one friend she depended on for support. She looked pained and began to deal. "I just wanted to make sure they were shuffled."

Mildred, arranging her hand, decided on a direct approach. "Did Birnbaum say anything about why you're so big? I wasn't that big at four months. Were you?" she said to Irene who shook her head.

Ida put down her cards. She hated Mildred. "If you must know, I'm having twins."

They stared at her. "Twins!"

Eleanor said, "And I can't even get preg!"

Irene said, "What's the matter with twins, Ida? Did Birnbaum say there could be a problem?"

Ida shook her head.

Mildred said that she would be upset too because it was hard enough to take care of one baby.

Ida picked up her cards. "Let's play."

Irene said, "One diamond."

Ida passed.

Mildred said, "Two babies." Even Ida had to laugh.

The games were in the afternoon, so the girls usually served a light snack, a lemon or lime Jell-O mold with Del Monte fruit cocktail embedded, or cottage cheese with extra-thin slices of cucumber, finely chopped celery and radish or tuna salad accompanied by zwieback crackers, plus coffee with cream and sugar. While Irene and Eleanor emptied the ashtrays, Mildred brought in her good plates, cups and saucers and silverware, then a casserole of steaming macaroni and American cheese.

The girls stared at this heavy repast. Mildred explained, "Ida is going to need the nourishment."

Ida, who they all knew was intent on not gaining weight, suspected Mildred of trying to sabotage her diet and ate only a "thimbleful." The others indulged, disregarding their six o'clock dinners. Ida lit a cigarette and watched them eat.

At dinnertime, in the kitchen of the Nollmans' second-floor flat, Charlie came home to boiled chicken, leftover from last night's chicken soup, boiled potatoes, canned peas and three-day-old iceberg lettuce slathered with French dressing. He said, "So how's things? You look a little tired." He glanced at the food, which did not bother him with his delicate stomach.

Ida was gratified that he had noticed her despondent mood. She had to tell him about the twins, and she began to cry.

He had adopted a patient tone when he addressed Ida's mood swings. "Sweetie, what is it?"

She sobbed out the news about the twins.

"Oh," he said and looked gloomy.

Ida was pleased that Charlie was not happy. She thought that he might be worried about the additional expense. But, in fact, he was concerned about sex. The larger Ida had grown, the less Charlie wanted to make love to her. He was uncomfortable about his lack of desire; a dread of impotence had always flickered at the edges of his consciousness.

Ida had never been aggressive about sex, never worn seductive lingerie. Charlie's pals, sitting with a drink in one hand and a cigar in the other, had swapped stories about removing black lace or red bras and panties from their writhing wives. Charlie was happier with a woman who never made a fuss in bed. In normal times, after making love, he would say, "Was that good?"

"Oh, yes, thank you," Ida would respond, and then turn over to go to sleep.

That night, she turned off the light before getting undressed. Like all of their friends, they slept in side-by-side twin beds. Charlie had wanted a double bed, but Ida wouldn't have it. "Ma and Pa sleep in a double bed," she had told him, ending the discussion.

In her bed, Ida was silent, but he could tell that she was not asleep. He reached out and touched her hip. She grabbed his hand and held it. Encouraged, he moved over to her bed and slid under the covers.

"Oh, Charlie," she said, "I'm so unhappy."

He kissed her shoulder. "Poor sweetie." He felt himself stiffening.

She was sobbing. "I don't want twins. What can we do?"

"It will be fine," he said. "You'll see. Just fine." He rubbed against her and touched her breast.

She twisted in his arms, weeping. "Oh, Charlie. Help me. I can't stand it."

"Poor sweetie," he repeated. "Poor sweetie." He could no longer lie on top of her, so he pushed and pulled until her back was toward him and he could enter her.

"Oh, Charlie," she murmured, still sobbing.

"Poor sweetie," he said, feeling greatly relieved.

Charlie's past had influenced his sense of ambivalence towards women. When he was ten years old, his father died of intractable asthma. He, his mother, his three sisters and two "aunts," distant relatives from the old country, lived in a three-room tenement apartment. Charlie shared a pallet with two of his sisters. He always knew what clothes to wear, how to hold his utensils, how to comb his hair and brush his teeth, using only a few drops of water that had to be lugged up three flights of stairs from the street, how to keep himself from belching or farting, how to accomplish a rapid bowel movement in the toilet on their floor that served two families, how to ignore the nudity of his sisters and of his mother, but not necessarily of his "aunts." He knew these things because there was always a woman around to instruct, prompt or criticize him, or in the case of one of his "aunts," to entice him. Charlie couldn't bear to live without women and had very mixed feelings about living with them. And he was tormented by what he considered an immoral, yet immense, sexual attraction to almost all women.

On the other hand, he panicked when pursued by an aggressive woman, especially if she was attractive. But then there was Martha Ulrich, a secretary at Warner Bros., a company in the film building where Charlie worked. Martha was a mousy, brown-haired, flat-chested shiksa with an urge. She wanted to have sex. She did not care about marriage and did not think about love. She knew that with her awkward body and plain looks, she did not attract men. She liked Charlie and could see by what happened with other girls on the floor that if approached, he would retreat.

Martha waited and watched until the day of the blizzard. It had started to snow after lunch. Within a few hours, there were three inches on the ground with a swirling wind and the snow turning to sleet. People were struggling to keep their footing. The Warner Bros. people began to leave.

On normal days the phones rang constantly. By four o'clock on this day, they were silent. After looking anxiously at the storm, most of the men headed for their cars and the treacherous drive home; most of the girls bundled up at bus and streetcar stops. Charlie continued to work. He did not admit to himself that he was reluctant to go home to Ida. Martha typed advertising copy that did not have to be finished that day. At 5:00 p.m., she asked Charlie if he would like a cup of tea. He was surprised and said sure. Both of them were aware that there was nobody else on the floor. With any other girl on the staff, Charlie would have been edgy. She went to the galley to make tea that she brought to his desk. He added sugar cubes from the box she brought, stirred in some milk and blew on the hot tea. "So," he said, "aren't you going home?"

"Sure," she responded. "But I needed to finish the ad copy. What about you?"

"Of course," he said. He looked at Martha to see if she was blaming him for not hurrying home to his pregnant wife. She sipped the tea, her eyes down and smiled a little smile.

"Probably we should get going while the going is good," he said and put his papers away into his desk drawer. She did the same. They rode the elevator down. When they reached the sidewalk, a gust of wind blew her against him.

"Oh, my," she said. "My goodness." She held on to his arm. He enjoyed the feeling of holding her up.

"How do you go?" he said.

"I take the bus." She peered at the snow and sleet. "If they're still running."

Charlie said, "I'll drive you home."

His Hupmobile was the last car left in the parking lot. He maneuvered onto the street, drove to Woodward Avenue and headed north. She emitted low "ohs and ahs" as he corrected for skids.

"You have to know how to drive on snow," he told her. He peered through his wipers that were beginning to stick. He glanced at her. She seemed worried. "I'll make it," he said.

She said she knew that and directed him to her building. He found a place to park and walked her to the door.

"Thank you, sir," she said. "I knew you were a gentleman."

"That's okay," he said. "My pleasure."

She seemed absorbed in the snowflakes, and he wondered what she was thinking. She smiled at him as if they had a shared secret. He smiled back. She said, "This really is terrible. Would you like another cup of tea before you head back into the storm?"

Charlie hesitated. "That sounds nice, but I really have to get home."

"Of course." She squeezed his arm. "And thanks again for being so nice."

Getting into the parking space was one thing; getting out was another. The symbolism was not lost on Charlie, and he tried hard to extricate his car. But after wearing deep ruts into the snow, he gave up and pressed the buzzer of Martha's apartment.

She brushed aside his apologies and said, "I'll make tea."

Charlie was tense. It took a while for Martha to find a topic that he was comfortable with. When she asked about his life in New York City, he grew restless. She did not want to remind him about his home life and his pregnant wife. Finally, she hit on sports and the Detroit Tigers.

"We're going to have a great team," he told her. "Are you really interested in the Tigers?"

"Oh, yes," she confessed. "I love Hank Greenberg."

"You do?"

She smiled sweetly. "He's so handsome. I shouldn't tell you this, but I'm partial to Jewish men."

He laughed. "Well, you're in the right business."

She glanced at her watch. "I have a custom. I like a little sherry now and then. Can I offer you a small glass?"

"Sherry?" He never drank sherry. "Sure, why not?"

Three drinks later, they were side by side on the couch and laughing. She put her hand on his arm and told him that she had always admired him. He felt manlier than he had in months. He could feel himself becoming erect. He thought, I wouldn't want to waste it.

Later, he phoned Ida and told her that he had driven a colleague home and that he would have to stay where he was parked until the street was cleared. He was pleased that he had sounded normal and was a little upset that she did not seem to be concerned and did not say that she missed him.

In fact, Charlie had not sounded normal to Ida. She heard tension in his voice. She sat at their kitchen table with a cup of coffee and a cigarette, replayed the conversation in her mind and considered the implications. Maybe he felt a little guilty because he had gone to a bar with his pals from the office and had a drink or two. Maybe not. For a moment, as if she had touched a hot steam iron, she considered the possibility that Charlie had been unfaithful and her pregnant with twins. *No, no, no*, she thought. *Not Charlie. Not her Charlie. He would never do that to her. He loved her. He took care of her.*

Nobody had ever told Ida about sex. Charlie was no help. He wanted to move around inside her, have an orgasm and withdraw, emotionally as well as physically. She had no idea of having pleasure from this act. She had no notion of being desirable. Her ideas about passion were grounded in romance novels and radio soap operas. In her secret world, love was betrayed, regularly. And she liked to play with the boundary between real life and true romance.

When Charlie at last came home late, complaining about the city's slowness in snow removal, she kissed him, but she was not happy. As the days went by, she sensed that something in their marriage had shifted. Something in Charlie was not the same. He was tense, then unexpectedly calm. He was caring, but at the same time, distant. Ida pondered explanations. She did not rush to a conclusion. She decided that Charlie had a secret. She could not bear to think that he had betrayed her. She was miserable and finally confided in her mother who had no doubt about what had happened. Bertha moved into the spare bedroom. In the evenings, she and Ida talked to each other as if Charlie weren't there.

Then Ida began to spot. Dr. Birnbaum ordered her to spend most of her time in bed. They moved the Philco into the bedroom. Bertha would join them for broadcasts of her favorite commentators, H. V. Kaltenborn and Gabriel Heater, whose gloomy assessments of the United States and the world fit the mood in the flat.

At night, Charlie walked alongside Ida when she went to the bathroom, his arm hovering close to hers, but not touching. He knew that he had stumbled seriously. He was miserable with the realization that it was too late for apologies or forgiveness. At times he writhed with what he considered very bad luck.

In Ida's ninth month, Dr. Birnbaum listened for a long time with his stethoscope. He told her that there might be a little problem and that he wanted to talk with her and Charlie together.

"I'm sure it's nothing," she told her gang that afternoon, sitting hugely on a bridge chair and emitting a long stream of cigarette smoke. The girls stopped and looked at her. "Play," she said angrily to Irene who dealt the cards.

At dinner, conversation between the three of them was sparse. Charlie applied butter to his mashed potatoes. He liked them just so. Ida told him that Dr. Birnbaum wanted to talk to them both. Charlie paused and asked what it was about. She assured him that it was nothing. He asked her when Birnbaum wanted to see him. Tomorrow, she told him. Her mother shook her head gloomily.

Charlie said, "I have a big day tomorrow.

"You've had a lot of big days." Ida sounded irritated. Charlie asked for the ketchup to go with his meatloaf. He was not going to ask any questions. She was staring at him and, surprisingly for her, was challenging him. He felt compelled to say something. He told her that it was a busy time at the company. She said that she knew that he had to work late even when there were snowstorms.

Charlie was rigid with a mouthful of mashed potatoes. Ida averted her gaze from him to the platter of meatloaf, somehow conveying the sensation that there was little difference between him and the ground beef. Ida seemed to swell in her chair. Charlie looked at her and at her mother, a woman whose moral authority was not to be challenged. In an act of metaphysical unity, of which he was dimly aware, Charlie swallowed his potatoes as his heart sank.

With Ida gloomy and frightened and Charlie miserable and flooded with guilt, they did not speak for the rest of the night. The next day, side by side in a thick silence, across the big desk from Dr. Birnbaum, they were having trouble grasping what he was telling them. "Did you hear what I said, Mr. Nollman?"

Charlie shook his head. "You said that you're concerned about one of the heartbeats?"

"Exactly."

Ida shuddered.

Charlie said, "What does that mean?"

Dr. Birnbaum came around the desk and took one of Ida's hands. He always did this at such moments. "It means that one of the fetuses may be in trouble."

They stared at him, not comprehending. "Well," Ida said, "it may only be a little slow."

"Hold on," Charlie said, emerging from his funk. "One of them is having a hard time?"

Dr. Birnbaum was relieved. He had never encountered such a dense couple among his Jewish patients. "Yes, that seems to be the situation."

Ida grasped what was being said. She considered that she was now carrying a sick being in her womb and fainted. When she revived, Dr. Birnbaum told them that Ida would have to come to Harper's Hospital on the next day for a caesarian. He promised that he would do his best to deliver two healthy, normal babies.

In the green waiting room, Charlie and Bertha sat on chrome and leather chairs among chattering families that included two men wearing black suits and hats and speaking Yiddish. Several of the visitors had brought picnic baskets and offered to share hard-boiled eggs, tuna sandwiches, apples and Vernor's Ginger Ale. Neither Charlie nor Bertha, who kept muttering, "Oy vey iz mir," could eat.

One baby was born dead; the other was healthy. Ida was sick, but would survive. Two weeks later, mother and child came home. Ida recovered slowly. She had to spend the next three months in bed. Bertha took care of little Freddie. Ida couldn't breastfeed; she had no milk or desire. Bertha sat in an old oak rocking chair with the baby on her lap, fed him infant formula and sang Yiddish lullabies from the old country.

For the first time in her life, Ida grieved. Charlie could not help and could not close the gap caused by her bitter certainty of betrayal.

"Oh, sweetheart," he kept repeating.

"What?" she said after a long pause. She studied his face as if she wanted him say something meaningful that would ease her pain.

"Would you like me to read to you?" he finally said.

"You decide." She turned her face to the wall.

He didn't know what to do, so he walked out of their bedroom.

At the office, the whole staff was supportive and gradually, at work at least, Charlie began to feel better. Martha, by this time, had senselessly turned her attentions to Cal, an overweight film booker, who thought that her awkward approaches were hilarious.

5. Hot Sun, Warm Sand

Charlie said, "I'll stay only twenty minutes in the sun, then I'll come under the umbrella."

After three days of rain, it was at last a clear, hot day in Miami Beach. Charlie, who took pride on being thinner than most men his age, sat in green bathing trunks, sunglasses and his Yankees cap, his toes dug into the warm sand. Ida and his sister, Lena, were completely hidden from the punishing sun by the red-and-orange striped umbrella the beach boy had planted for them close to the water.

Charlie and Lena were talking about the old days on the Lower East Side. Ida, who was covered with lotion and white towels and wearing a broad-brimmed straw hat, was content to listen for the moment. Anyway, she and Charlie had a certain matter to discuss with Lena.

"Poor Max," Lena began.

Charlie looked at his sister. "So, Lena, now you're grieving?"

Lena, who was wrapped in a yellow beach robe, managed a little smile. "I can't be such a hypocrite."

Charlie didn't mind noting the obvious. "Especially after he left you all the money, Lena."

Lena rolled over to look at him. "Who else was he going to leave it to? One of his models? After forty-two years, I should have it. Right?"

Ida chipped in, "You're going to have plenty of men knocking on your door, Lena, a rich widow."

Lena studied a cloud that floated in front of their sun. She sighed. "I'm thinking about when the shadkin came to Ma about Max. I was twenty-one already. We were sitting in our kitchen, and the shadkin says, 'Missus, have I got a man for your Lena. Max Tannenbaum. A prize.'"

Charlie said to Ida, "In case you don't know, shadkins were marriage brokers."

Ida didn't think she needed lessons in Yiddish just because she didn't grow up in New York. "Don't I know that? We had shadkins in Detroit."

Lena didn't want to be diverted. "Max was already a big shot in the garment trade," she continued. "That was enough for Ma. And you know what it was like in that tenement."

"He was a head shorter than you," Charlie said. "He liked tall women."

"The man was a goat," Lena shrugged.

"He liked his models," Charlie said.

Lena sighed. "In seven years, I had five babies, what could I do? I couldn't keep up, even with a girl to help me."

"We didn't know where Max lived anymore," Charlie said.

Lena pulled her feet back under the umbrella where the sun was advancing. "Not in his home," she said. "That I can tell you."

"I don't know how you put up with it," Ida said. "On the other hand, maybe it explains what's going on now."

Lena glared at her. "What? What's going on now, if you don't mind?"

Ida suddenly was absorbed in a fishing smack bobbing on the horizon.

Lena said, "What's going on, Ida?"

Ida would not look at her. She said, "Charlie . . ."

Charlie dug his feet into the sand. "Lena," he said, "don't take offense."

Lena was grim. "You're my brother, Charlie. That doesn't give you and Ida the right to interfere."

Ida smiled. "Lena, we know that you're vulnerable now."

"Vulnerable?" Lena's voice rose an octave. "Vulnerable? You're telling me that I'm vulnerable?"

Charlie was soothing. "New widows, Lena, don't always show good judgment."

Lena took a deep breath. "I assume that the two of you are referring to my friend Helmut."

"Helmut?" Charlie said.

Ida said, "Charlie, the blond lifeguard's name is Helmut."

"Isn't that a German name?" he said.

Lena was irritated. "He's Swedish."

"Thank God," Charlie said.

Lena shook her finger at him. "Listen, you don't have to worry about me. I know what I'm doing."

"Lena, how do you think it looks, for Christ's sake," Charlie said. "Helmut looks like your son, except for the blond hair."

Lena was emphatic. "Charlie. I don't care how it looks, really I don't."

Charlie tried for a brotherly tone. "What do you have to talk about? What do you have in common?"

Lena laughed at him. "We have in common what matters, if you must know."

Ida shook her head. "A woman in her seventies."

"And making up for lost time," Lena said. "Why not, Ida?"

Charlie shrugged. "Why not? Why not?" He looked hard at Ida and turned to his sister. "I guess you're entitled."

Lena smiled. "Thank you, Charlie." She said, "At first, my marriage was okay. But all those kids . . . I couldn't keep them quiet. The house was hell. Max wanted a little peace."

Ida frowned. "I don't know why you're being kind to him. The man certainly didn't care about you or your kids."

Lena sat up. "Listen, Ida, you have no reason to feel sorry for me. What about you and Charlie? I haven't heard anyone say that your marriage was made in heaven."

"Lena," Charlie was irritated. "That's not necessary."

"Charlie," Lena said, "who cares? Who's pointing fingers? Have you forgotten what it was like for us? None of us married for love. Who could be so stupid? All we knew was that we had to get out of that place. Am I right?"

Charlie held up his arms, imploring the assistance of the Almighty. "Listen, Lena, God knows that Ida, and I just want to help."

"With what?" Lena demanded. "What do I need help with?"

"Not with grieving." Ida was cool now.

"Not with grieving," Lena agreed. "Not that I didn't want more in my marriage from Max, a little tenderness, once in a while, now and then."

Charlie was sympathetic. "Being married to Max wasn't easy."

"Well, Charlie," she said. "At least my Max got you your haberdasher job."

Charlie stared into the distance. "I think I'll go for a swim," he said.

Lena laughed. "If you get into trouble, Helmut will rescue you."

Part Five:
Seven Oaks

1. Thank You, Larry King

Ida put two containers of frozen food into the microwave and said, "Forget it, Freddie. I'm not leaving my home."

Remembering a kitchen of plenty, Fred considered the Chicken Kiev and beef stew to be symptomatic of his mother's decline. Already upset by her refusal to listen to him, he resumed their ongoing dispute, although he knew it was useless. "You fall now, Mom. What if you can't get up? What happens then? Will I have to come over and pick you up off the floor?"

She stared at the ticking microwave clock. "I can take care of myself. Which one do you want, Freddie?" He left after eating the beef stew. He couldn't stand the Chicken Kiev.

In bed, Ida reached for her pain pills and didn't stop until she overdosed for the second time in three months.

A nurse phoned Fred from the emergency room. "Ida's here again, Mr. Nollman."

"Is she in bad shape?"

"We pumped her out. She'll be okay after she gets a little rest."

"How did you know to come and get her?"

"She called 911 after she took the pills."

"Wasn't the door locked?"

"She unlocked it."

"She's too much. I'll come in a few hours."

"Bring some clothes for her," the nurse said.

He waited in the emergency room lobby while they got Ida dressed. She emerged through sliding doors on a wheelchair pushed by an aide and looking everywhere, but at him. He helped her to his car, holding her ice-cold hand.

Fred drove without speaking. He walked her to her house and said good night in a flat voice. Ida cried, but got herself into bed. She fell asleep with the TV on and awoke to laughter on *The Morning Show*. "What could be so funny?" she said to the TV set.

Fred called Sarah who came and made her sister tunafish salad on toasted white bread with tea. Ida was red-eyed and wearing a quilted yellow robe and matching slippers. When she tried to lift her teacup, her hand shook, and she had to set it down. Sarah left without discussing what had happened last night or the rattling teacup.

Ida went back to bed and decided to talk to Larry King whom she had chosen to be her consultant.

Larry, it's me.

Ida, what's the matter?

I didn't mean to take so many pills. It was a mistake.

I'll say.

When I realized what I had done, I called 911.

Ida, I have to tell you something that you are definitely not going to want to hear.

I know what you're going to say, Larry.

I don't think so. Listen, Ida, what is going to happen, my dear, is that you are going to force your beloved son to commit you.

He wouldn't.

He would. With more provocation, he will. Even though you're sure that Fred has the patience of a saint.

What can I do? I don't want to leave my home.

Do what he says. Go to a senior residence. For your own good.

I know what's good for me. I hate the idea.

I don't think you have a choice.

I'll consider it.

Do that, Ida.

2. Seven Oaks

Whenever Fred phoned Ida before noon, her speech was mushy, almost incoherent. So he knew that she had been overdoing it with her pills during the night.

To head off more visits to the ER, he scanned the internet for senior facilities in their area. He saw this promotion: "Hey, folks. You can have it all at the Seven Oaks Home for Seniors. We're the gracious and affordable alternative in living for seniors. Are you looking for companionship and a lot of fun, more choices of interesting and challenging activities than you can imagine and superb dining? We guarantee it. There's no need for withdrawal and seclusion. Seven Oaks means engagement in life. So come on. We're waiting for you. The welcome mat is out."

Bullshit, he thought. *But maybe not bad.*

The next day, he toured the facility and signed up Ida, paying two months' security and a month's rent in advance. She had been living on his monthly contribution, plus her Social Security. His father, Charlie, the big spender, five years deceased, had saved almost nothing and cashed in his insurance, which wasn't much to start with. When Ida had asked, "What happened to all the money?" Fred changed the subject.

Ida was scheduled to move to Seven Oaks in two weeks. Time enough to get her packed, Fred reasoned.

"I know what it's like there," she said when he came to show her the place. "And I'm not going."

Mrs. Smithers, the assistant director, a tall, gray-haired black woman, was their guide. She kept calling Ida "dear."

"There's a lot going on here, Freddie." Ida seemed impressed. Fred nodded and said nothing.

To Mrs. Smithers, as they viewed the big dining room, Ida said, "I have friends here. They tell me the food is pretty good."

"We've hired the chef from the Statler Sheraton, dear," Mrs. Smithers purred.

"Not that I eat much," Ida murmured.

Fred had warned Mrs. Smithers that he hadn't told his mother she was already enrolled. But Mrs. Smithers was a strong believer in the inevitable. "Would you like to see the apartment we've set aside for you?"

"You have an apartment for me?" Ida said. "What have you done, Freddie?"

"We just want you to look at it, Mom."

Ida sighed. Her son had decided her fate without consulting her. She discussed this with her dead husband: "Charlie, you wouldn't have done that, would you? I'm just a bother to him. He wants me out of the way. I'm helpless. Do you know who's here? Mitzi Ginsberg. If she's here, it can't be all bad, right?"

"C11," Mrs. Smithers said, unlocking the door.

It was a one-bedroom apartment. The living room and bedroom were spacious; sliding glass doors opened onto the big front lawn. Sunlight streamed in.

After watching Ida inspect the rooms, Mrs. Smithers said, "Are you a plant person, dear?"

Ida nodded. She was silent now. The reality of moving into this bare apartment had gripped her. "Oh, God," she murmured.

Mrs. Smithers glided to her side and took her hand. Ida was startled. *What is she doing?*

"What am I doing?" Ida said.

"Mom?" Fred said. "What is it?"

Mrs. Smithers stroked her hand. "I know," she whispered. "I know."

"I can't do it, Freddie," Ida moaned.

"Oh, Mom," Fred said. "Only if you want to."

For a moment, Ida looked hopeful.

"Shh," Mrs. Smithers whispered. "Nobody wants to. Am I right?" she said to Ida.

Ida nodded.

"But there comes a time, dear, doesn't there?" Mrs. Smithers was so sympathetic. Fred and Ida stared. Mrs. Smithers shook her head. "There just comes a time when we need a little help. Isn't that true?"

Ida grabbed her purse, hunting for a tissue. Mrs. Smithers was there first with a whole box of Kleenex that somehow was available on the windowsill.

Mrs. Smithers watched Ida use three sheets of tissue. "And that's why there's a Seven Oaks."

It spite of her misery, Ida was impressed by what she realized was a skilled performance. "Yes, I see." She surprised Fred by winking at him.

"What do you think of the place, Mom?" He wanted Ida to confirm what she was on the verge of saying.

"It's fine, sweetheart," Ida told him. "But what about all my things?"

Mrs. Smithers told Fred. "It's terrible to have to move from a house to a one-bedroom apartment. Of course, your mother is upset."

Ida reflected that whatever happened, she still had her pills, thank God. She wished she could take some now.

Fred, who did not want to let go of this moment, said, "Lots of closets, Mom."

"Tiny kitchen," Ida muttered.

Mrs. Smithers reassured her, "You'll have lunch and dinner in the dining room, dear. There won't be much need to cook."

Walking back to the entrance, Ida said, "Excuse me," and went up to a group of women standing in the lobby next to a fountain that featured a mermaid spouting water. "Mitzi?" she said.

A stout, gray-haired woman leaning on a walker said, "Ida? What are you doing here?"

Ida smiled wanly. "I'm coming."

The woman nodded. "Well, this place isn't so bad. Are you telling her the truth, Mrs. Smithers?" She had come up behind them.

"Absolutely." Mrs. Smithers laughed lightly.

Mitzi smiled. "Do you still play bridge, Ida? There are good players here."

"Yes," Ida said. "Well, that's nice."

As they moved to the entrance, Mitzi called after them, "We have a reading group, Ida. Maybe you'll join."

Ida waved her assent. Fred stifled his impulse to comment on his mother's change of heart.

Ida noticed that she was being watched by two of the male residents. One, leaning on a cane, was even smiling at her. She stared at him in the moment of leaving. Meshuga, she thought. *A bissel coocoo.* The man's image stayed with her on the way back to her apartment. "The last thing I want," she reflected.

3. The Miracle

Sarah moved with Ida to Seven Oaks. "If you can talk her into going there," she had told Fred. "I'll go too."

Even with her wandering eye, Sarah was a talkative person and met a lot of people right away. Ida was not good at small talk.

"You can discuss the weather and the food," she told Sarah. "I'm not that kind of person."

"What kind of person are you, Ida?"

"I guess I'm a little choosy." Ida sighed. "Do you mind?"

"You've been drifty again," Sarah warned her. "And you're slurring your words."

"No," Ida said.

"The staff has noticed."

"What?" Ida was shocked.

Sarah warned her. "If they decide that you're an addict, they'll throw you out."

Not possible, Ida was sure until Fred told her that he had been summoned to a meeting with Mrs. Smithers, who had shown Ida the place, and her boss, Mr. Flowers.

Fred was grim. "If you don't stop with the pills, they're going to tell you to leave."

That could have happened because under stress, Ida took more pills. But the social worker, Mrs. Feldstein, appeared. A slender gray-haired woman in a tweed skirt and brown cashmere sweater, she took Ida to arts and crafts.

This gave rise to a series of fanciful ceramic animals made from molds and painted in vivid primary colors that formed a menagerie on Ida's dresser. Next came a series of surprisingly skillful watercolors that Ida adapted from pictures in magazines. When arts and crafts had a sale, she made seventeen dollars to Sarah's amazement.

After a few weeks, miracle of miracles, Ida walked through Seven Oaks like a veteran. She was struck by the change in how time moved. At home, minutes and hours fused, the clock was meaningless. She hardly knew day from night. Here she was busy; she had appointments! She dashed from arts and crafts to trips via the Seven Oaks van to the supermarkets, local shops and galleries. She signed up for a "See the Fall Leaves" bus tour of New England. She went to bingo in the recreation room on Thursday nights and old-time films in the lounge on Saturday nights. In bed, at last, she liked to itemize everything she had done on that day. She had time for her pills at night, but not during the day. She knew that after so long, she had come back to life. What luck. She had never dreamed it could happen.

That her life had changed was confirmed when a man sat next to her in the lounge. She recognized him. "You're the one who looked at me when we came to visit Seven Oaks."

"I'm Mendy Rubin," he said. "I've been here for six months. I can show you the ropes." He liked to talk and wave his cane for emphasis. "You're a good-looking woman," he told her. "In fact, I'm looking for a girlfriend."

Ida stared at him. "You'll have to find someone else." She stood. "I'm not in the market, if you don't mind."

Mendy nodded. "Easy come, easy go."

As Ida moved away, he called after her, "Plenty of fish in the sea."

Ida told Sarah about the encounter. "I knew he was meshuga."

Sarah was a little wistful. "At least you have a man who's interested in you."

"I'll send him to you," Ida told her sister. "We'll see what you have to say then."

Later, she wondered why she was thinking about Mendy Rubin. She shook her head. "Definitely not my type. Oh, well, like he said, 'Plenty of fish in the sea.'" She laughed out loud at how much she was enjoying life at Seven Oaks.

4. The Bread Fight

In the dining room, Ida and Sarah were seated with Jean Green and Doris Ratner who were notable for their violet-tinted hair. It was Jean who threw the first slice of bread. For days after each meal, she had said, "Do you mind," and would reach for the uneaten bread and rolls on the plates of her table partners, plus whatever was left in the bread basket . She would carry this trove in a large reclosable plastic bag to her room. She never offered an explanation.

After a week of witnessing Jean's bread-and-roll gathering and saying nothing, Ida and Sarah began to exchange looks and shrugs. Jean noticed, but ignored this silent commentary. Her friend Doris began to worry because of the tension that arose as they finished each meal.

The climax came when Jean reached for an uneaten roll on Ida's bread plate, and Ida grabbed it first. The two women glared at each other. Jean requested the roll. Ida, whose confidence at Seven Oaks had been growing steadily, refused. Jean reached into her plastic bag, and bread and rolls began to fly. Staff members ran to separate the combatants. Ida and Sarah were flushed and laughing. The other two were grim; Jean was holding back tears.

Later, at a "reconciliation" meeting in the game room, Ida demanded to know why Jean was hoarding the bread and rolls. Jean said it was nobody's business and that she was certainly not going to discuss the matter. Mrs. Smithers, the associate director, said that Seven Oaks would not tolerate another such public dispute and made the four women promise to suspend hostilities. She did agree that Jean was entitled to her privacy about her motives in this matter, but expressed concern that old bread and rolls might attract vermin.

Jean guaranteed that her cache was safe from mice and rats and had nothing more to say about the matter.

The next day at lunch, the four women ate in stony silence. When the meal ended, Ida and Sarah waited to see what Jean would do. When she reached for the breadbasket, Ida covered it with her hand.

"Well," Jean breathed, picked up the bread and rolls from the basket on the next table and quickly left the dining room.

"She's crazy," Ida said.

"What are we going to do?" Sarah said.

"I have a plan," Ida told her.

She whispered in Sarah's ear.

"Perfect," Sarah said.

That night after dessert, residents from the nearby tables gathered around Jean who twisted and stared at the throng. Trembling, she said, "What's going on?"

Ida said, "Now!"

The diners pressed around Jean, who began to scream, and emptied their breadbaskets on her plate. Jean ran out of the room.

It was the end of the bread-and-roll gathering. Neither Ida nor Sarah ever learned why Jean was hoarding her loot. Days later, Doris let it be known that Jean had once confided that she was concerned about a famine at Seven Oaks. When confronted, Jean totally denied this, but seriously discussed her dead mother's concern about the starving masses in Russia.

Ida told Sarah that contrary to her expectations, Seven Oaks certainly did not seem to be a boring place. "A little nuts," she said, "but definitely not boring."

5. Mother's Day

It was Mother's Day. Middle-aged children and grandchildren with shrill voices were visiting at the Sunday lunch. Ida compared her Fred with other men his age, particularly with Jean Green's son, Henry. Fred stood out because of his mop of white hair and broad shoulders. He had put on more bulk than Ida considered healthy, but so had the other sons with their oversized stomachs pushing out of their patterned sport jackets. Henry Green was the exception. He was totally bald and still thin, in fact gaunt. Ida knew that this was because of his ulcer. Ironically, he looked fitter than the other sons.

For her part, Jean Green had noticed that Ida's Fred had brought with him a short, gray-haired woman who, in her opinion, definitely should not have been wearing pants. Jean had heard that Fred had found a replacement for his wife, Nadine, whom everyone knew had left him. Jean thought, *Ida must be beside herself. Why doesn't this one color her hair and try to look halfway decent? My Henry would never be seen with such a frump.*

Jean savored Fred Nollman's well-known heartbreak over Nadine's desertion. *At least,* she thought, *Henry's wife, Agnes, didn't leave him, unless you count dying as leaving someone.*

Henry did. Whenever he thought about Agnes, the residue of his ulcer, usually dormant in what was left of his stomach, acted up.

Jean thought, *At least my Henry is glad to be with me.* She had watched when Fred walked in with his lady friend and saw his frown, then his pasted-on smile when Ida opened her arms so that he had to embrace her.

At Ida's table, Fred told his mother what she already knew, but had decided to ignore: that Henry was there with Jean Green.

Ida pretended that she couldn't see that far. "Does he still look sick?"

Fred laughed. "What's the matter with him, anyway?"

"Bleeding ulcer, dear," she told him. "They had to cut out most of his stomach."

The other two women were listening. Sarah said, "Jean is watching us. Don't look at them."

Audrey, Fred's girlfriend, said, "What are we talking about? Who is Jean?"

Sarah nodded toward Jean's table. "That woman with the purple hair. She's with her son, Henry. It's a sad story."

Audrey objected. "There are two women with purple hair."

"The skinny one," Sarah hissed. "The other one is Doris. She's always with Jean."

Ida said, "We used to be in the same crowd. Freddie never liked Henry, did you, dear? And now the two of them don't associate. Nothing really changes."

"Jean was jealous of you back then," Sarah added.

Audrey shrugged. She decided that these old quarrels were too hard to sort out and didn't much matter, anyway.

Jean saw that Ida and the others at her table had been looking at her and Henry. She stared at them and was pleased that they now were carefully looking elsewhere. Jean turned to her son. "Henry, I talked to our chef, William. William is from the islands, and he's making you a special order of steamed veggies with some of his local herbs."

Henry made a face. "I can't wait."

Anticipating rejection, Jean frowned. To divert him, she said, "Have you noticed Freddie Nollman's girlfriend?"

Henry hooted. "Nadine was a lot sexier."

"He was always jealous of you, Henry."

"He was always a jerk," he assured her.

Fred was in a reverie. He remembered when he was a kid, and he and his mother were visiting the Greens. The boys were on the front lawn. Henry, who was bigger, challenged him to a wrestling match. Fred was not a fighter and suspected that matters would not end well, but he was not about to back away. They grappled and fell to the ground. Fred was on top. Henry gave up without a struggle. Fred had the sense that all of the air had come out of Henry who began to cry and had run into his house. After a few minutes, Ida came out. "What did you do to him?"

"Nothing." Fred couldn't understand why his mother was yelling at him. "I didn't do anything. What did he say?"

"He said you don't fight fair."

Fred explained, "Henry wanted to wrestle. Then for no reason, he gave up, Mom. And he cried and ran into the house."

His mother nodded. "I know. He's a strange boy. But his mother adores him. Well, I don't blame her, even though he makes things up."

Fred felt better. It was not often that his mother made the effort to understand him. And on top of that, he had defeated Henry Green in a fair fight.

The wrestling match was an episode he never forgot. He wondered if Audrey would want to listen to the story. Probably not. He wished that Seven Oaks served wine with their meals. For whatever reason, none of the residents seemed to have retained their taste for alcohol. He sipped his Diet Coke.

As usual, Jean was poking at her food. Doris urged her to eat. "You're a toothpick. You've got to eat a little."

Jean hated it when Doris told her she should eat more. In an overbright voice, she said, "How are your veggies, Henry? They look positively yummy."

Then she worried that this was too close to the kind of baby talk he hated.

Henry shrugged, choosing not to make an issue of his eating. And he would not admit that the steamed vegetables tasted better than he expected. He pushed the plate away with the food half eaten and surprised Jean by standing up. "Let's go over there," he told his mother and Doris. "I want to hear what he has to say about Nadine."

Jean shuddered, but she and Doris followed him.

Fred saw that Jean, Henry and Doris were approaching his table. He looked at Ida and Sarah to see what they were thinking. They were sitting stiffly, but Ida was ready. "Well, Henry, it's nice to see you again. It's been a while, hasn't it?"

Jean wouldn't stand for any insinuation that her son was an infrequent visitor. "My Henry is so busy at his office. He doesn't have time to breathe."

Henry moved to outflank Ida. "Hello, Sarah. I heard you decided to move to Seven Oaks."

Sarah's bad eye wobbled in its orbit. She aligned herself with her sister. "Henry, what a treat to see you again."

Jean felt as though she were in a bubble. She could not deal with the crosscurrents. She wished that Henry had not brought them over to Ida's table.

Henry smiled at Audrey whom he did not perceive as a threat. She smiled back at him, puzzled.

Since they were ignoring her, Sarah decided to make some noise. "Where is that Ruby? I want to order dessert."

It was as if she hadn't spoken. Henry directed a question to Fred. "How is Nadine doing?"

Fred straightened in his chair. "I wouldn't know." He guessed what Henry had in mind and decided to beat him to it. "Why don't you give her a call? I'm sure she'd love to hear from you."

Henry was surprised. "I may do that. I always thought she was a sexy lady, right Mom?"

This was too fast for Jean. "I never thought about it, dear."

Fred muttered to Audrey, "Serve them both right."

Ida was looking around. "There's Ruby pouring coffee." She waved her fork in the air.

Fred pretended to be friendly. "You know, Henry, I was just thinking about that wrestling match we had a long time ago."

Henry shook his head. "What are you talking about?"

Audrey didn't want to be left out. "What wrestling match, Fred?"

He smiled. "In front of the Green's house when we were kids."

Audrey realized that Fred had a hidden motive. "Why are you talking about that?"

"Because he's still a jerk," Henry told her.

"I remember," Ida said. "Henry came running into the house crying."

Jean was furious. "Your Freddie didn't fight fair."

Henry was in retreat. "That was a long time ago." To Audrey, he said, "Nice to meet you." He said goodbye to Ida and Sarah and steered Jean back toward their table. He said, "Damn," and slowly sank to his knees as if the air inside him was escaping, like when he wrestled Fred.

Jean screamed. At Ida's table, they jumped to their feet. Henry sighed and sprawled full length on the floor. Aides came running, and one of them turned Henry onto his back. He was deathly white. His breathing was shallow. Ruby arrived and announced that 911 had been called. Jean slid down on the floor next to Henry. Doris said, "Jean, get up. What are you doing?"

"If he dies, I'm going to die too," Jean said.

Fred said to Audrey, "Can you believe this?"

Ida said to Sarah, "I don't know what to do."

Sarah said, "There is nothing to do. Why do you have to do something?"

Ida said, "I wanted this to be a nice Mother's Day."

Fred heard her. "It is a nice Mother's Day, Mother. Henry just can't stand losing."

Henry revived. He sat up and called out to Fred, "You're still a jerk."

Two aides lifted him to his feet. He was wobbly, but walked to his table with Jean and Doris following.

Jean was weeping. Doris twittered like a demented sparrow. "Oh, my. Oh, my. Oh, my."

The Seven Oaks nurse, stethoscope flashing, arrived with an assistant, a man who was pushing a gurney. Henry refused to let the nurse examine him. She turned her attention to Jean who had slumped in her chair. The nurse felt her pulse and listened to her heart. "Call the hospital," she said to her assistant. "I think she's having a heart attack."

"Oh, my God," Doris said, as they carried out Jean on the gurney.

At Ida's table, they were at a loss for words. Finally, Sarah said to Ruby, "We may as well have our dessert."

"Okay," Ruby said. "Chocolate ice cream or peach pie, or both, everyone?"

6. Fred

It had been two months, one week, four days and seventeen hours since Nadine had packed her bags and moved four blocks away to a small furnished apartment. Always a private person, she did not explain her move. This did not surprise Fred. But he expected her to come back after a few weeks, and it had begun to dawn on him that he was waiting in vain.

Hints about her reasons for leaving him began to dribble out when they met in restaurants, generally at breakfasts in their neighborhood diner, and during occasional phone calls: "We ran out of things to talk about, Fred. I'm sure it happens to a lot of couples after a long marriage." And "Don't blame yourself, Fred. This is something I had to do." And "We're both going to be better off. Don't laugh. You know I'm always right." And "Fred, You know that I wasn't happy. I need a chance to be happy."

He felt jumpy and numb at the same time. He waited for her phone calls. But something in her voice alarmed him one day when she asked to meet for breakfast. "Something I need to discuss . . ."

Something. He knew her so well. Something in her voice.

He had slept poorly as usual when he dreaded an encounter with Nadine. Over coffee, a little nervously, but determined, she said, "I've met somebody, Fred."

Simple as that. Met somebody, Fred. "I see."

"I love him."

Well, that's that, isn't it? "Okay, goodbye."

"Where are you going?"

"What?"

"Please don't leave like that. We have to talk about things."

Bizarre. She wants to have a conversation. "Goodbye, Nadine."

Growing up, Fred had always confided in Sarah, and occasionally he still phoned her to talk about his troubles. She had an infallible instinct for how to increase his aggravation, which, perversely, was why he wanted to talk with her. He wanted his angst deepened and increased. It was circular, the worse he felt, the more justified he believed he was in feeling that way.

She told him, "Freddy, you've always been too good for your own good."

He felt satisfactorily gloomy. "I never expected it."

"So where did she move to?"

"Not far." He was slightly hysterical. "We'll probably meet each other at Farmer Jack's."

Sarah spoke intimately into the phone. "Freddie, shall I tell you what you did wrong?"

"What?" *No fair, Sarah.* He was worried she was going to hurt him.

Sarah had always loved Fred and was enraged on his behalf. "I told you this before," she said in a loud voice. "You can't spend your life trying to please people, especially someone like Nadine."

He was miserable. "I wanted to make her happy."

Sarah felt that her point was made. "And she left you."

"It's what she wants," he said quietly.

"Freddie! Darling, what do *you* want?"

He slumped over the phone, pressing against the mouthpiece. "I want Nadine to come back. What kind of life is this?"

She said, "Life can be so unfair, isn't that right? I know all about it."

He sensed that she was enjoying something in this conversation and began to pull himself out of his funk. "Well, I still have a lot of good years ahead of me."

"Of course you do," she agreed. "Are you coming to dinner on Friday night?"

"I guess so. I promised Mom that I would."

"It will be wonderful to see you, darling."

"Right."

Fred hated Seven Oaks. He knew that his mother was thriving, but visits to her upset him. Some of the residents, probably most of them, he had to admit, were reasonably alert and walked fairly well; some of them stepped right along. But others, the ones he hated to look at, had slipped into a semi-infirmity of mind or body. He didn't know why they bothered him so. Was he seeing his own fate? Was he destined to be like these people, listless, distracted riders in wheelchairs who did not care where they were being pushed by aides who were uninterested in their passengers and became animated only when they had an opportunity to gossip among themselves?

For Fred, the worst were the people whose minds ranged from dim to blank. A cluster of these dotty folks sat patiently, a few leaning precariously on padded benches around the main entrance, intent on comings and goings.

Welcome to Seven Oaks, he thought. *And why do they have to be the first thing you see when you come here?*

In the big dining room, walking slowly with Ida and Sarah to the table on the far wall, Fred was stared at by half of the population of Seven Oaks. Ida loved it, of course, loved showing off her handsome son who had come to dinner with his mother.

She had entreated him. "Friday night, Freddie. Everyone's children are coming. You haven't eaten here in a month."

He put up with the bland, unseasoned, under or overcooked food. He tried not to look at residents at nearby tables who had to be fed by their aides. And he listened to Ida's complaints about the food and the service. "What can you expect?" About the reduction of fresh linen from once a week to once every two weeks. "That's terrible, Mom. How can they do that?" About snubs by women who were independently wealthy. About inferior bridge players. About the young woman in charge of arts and crafts. "She's mean to me."

"Do you want me to talk to the director?"

"No, what good would that do?"

"It can't hurt, Mom."

"Please don't bother. It's not so bad."

Sarah laughed. "She likes it here. She just doesn't want to give you the satisfaction."

Fred yawned. They both told him that he looked tired. He confessed that he hadn't slept much the past week. This elicited a series of comments of concern by his mother and aunt amid mentions that he had to get over Nadine.

Ida told him that she was worried about him driving home.

He told her not to be silly, that he was a good driver.

She held his arm as they walked to the entrance. "Go right home, sweetheart, and get some sleep."

He nodded and yawned. "Right. Good night, Mom."

After dinner, Sarah and Ida sat outside of the dining room. Sarah said, "Does he tell you anything?"

"Nothing. He tells me nothing. I don't ask."

"I don't understand Nadine's generation," Sarah complained. "After all these years. She's fifty."

Ida sighed deeply. "He says she's looking for happiness. To me, it sounds like a soap opera."

"Happiness? Happiness? I don't believe it."

"That's what she said."

"Happiness? What's happiness? Who has happiness?"

"I wouldn't know."

"Who needs happiness?" Sarah was outraged. "A child."

In the parking lot, Fred was on the verge of hyperventilating. No good deed goes unpunished, he assured himself, sitting in his car, telling himself to calm down. He started the motor and had a fantasy of ramming right into the Seven Oaks lobby. He shook his head and drove slowly to the highway. It was a two-lane road. Fred was conscious of wavering in his lane. He slowed, but the car behind him honked. He speeded up and blinked at the headlights of the oncoming traffic. He yawned deeply and planned to pull off at the gas station at the next intersection. He yawned again. He remembered when he was dating Nadine and drove home late at night and used to stick his head out of the window to keep from falling asleep.

The next thing he knew he was assaulted by a strong noxious smell and pinned in his seat by his air bag. Some men were running around the car and shouting. One of them pried open his door and asked if he were okay. Fred looked around and saw that he had run into a roadside telephone pole. Obviously his car was seriously damaged. He himself was sore where the seat belt had grabbed him, but otherwise unhurt. "My God," he murmured.

At home, in bed, after two painkilling pills, he knew that he had been lucky. The cops had told him, "You could have run into an oncoming car." He knew they were right. As it was, he was going to get a ticket. And he would have to deal with the insurance company. He closed his eyes and let the pills do their thing.

"I've got to start over," he realized before he fell asleep.

7. The Return of Josh

Ida and Sarah were watching TV in the lounge when a man came up behind them and said, "Hello, Sarah." She turned and stared until she realized that it was Josh Greenberg whom she had last seen when she was twenty and never expected to see again in a million years. He did not look like the Josh she had known. He had added a lot of bulk, lost most of his hair, wore thick glasses and leaned on a cane. She did not know whether to laugh or cry and did a little of both.

Ida came to her rescue. "I remember you, mister."

"And I remember you," he said. "You're the snooty sister."

She laughed. "You're the one with too much color in his cheeks. So Ma was wrong. You didn't die of tuberculosis."

He smiled. "You still put your cards on the table."

"That's right. Are you single now? Maybe it's not too late for you and Sarah."

At that point, Sarah, who had been listening in a daze, lost it. She screamed at Ida, "Are you crazy? What are you talking about?" She turned to him, "I'm so sorry. Please don't listen to anything my sister says."

Ida was calm. "What are you yelling about?"

Josh spoke to Sarah. "I saw you across the room, and I thought, 'I know her.' How are you?"

It took some effort, but she regained control. "I'm fine, Josh. How are you? It's nice to see you again. What are you doing here?"

"I'm visiting a friend, Henny Lieberman. She's new at Seven Oaks."

Sarah was impressed at how at ease he seemed. The Josh she remembered had been tense and urgent.

He said as much. "I've changed more than you have, not just physically."

In fifty years, she had simply grown into an older version of herself, the way she held herself, head up, shoulders back; her smile slow, hesitant; her hair gray, now, but still clipped short; her manner calm, watchful, holding herself back, keeping her distance, her bad eye averted. It was still Sarah.

Looking at him, she couldn't help agreeing. "You've changed a lot, Josh."

He said, "We should talk. Catch up? How about it?" Was there an edge in his voice? Could he still be angry that she had walked away?

She thought about his offer. "I don't think so. What's the point?"

Ida said, "Sarah, what's the matter with you? What do you have to lose?"

He nodded. "Right again, sister. I've forgotten your name."

"Ida. Ida Haberman," she said. "I'm a widow, Josh."

Josh smiled and looked at Sarah. "May I phone you?"

She was silent, looked worried and then nodded yes.

"That's almost where we left off," he said.

As he had done fifty years ago, he phoned the next day. They sat side by side in the lounge, talked quietly and were surprisingly comfortable.

"I've had three wives," he told her. "I have seven grandchildren, four boys, three girls. Do you want to know their names?"

"I don't think so." She smiled and told him that she had never married.

"Ah," he said. "I'm sorry."

She said, "Maybe I shouldn't have sent you away."

"You might have spared me all those divorces."

"You might have had four wives."

"We'll never know." He laughed.

He filled in his successful career as an architect. His travels around the world, his heart attack.

He said what they had both been thinking, how strange it was to meet again after so many years.

"We've lived our lives," she suggested.

"Yes, except maybe we're not quite finished. Listen, why don't we make a date to go to the movies?"

"Oh, God." She sighed.

"I owe you," he said. "We were going to see Ginger Rogers that night."

"That's true." She laughed for the first time. "But I don't think so." She touched his hand and, walking deliberately, her head high, left him sitting in the lounge.

The next day, in Ida's room, Sarah would not discuss her conversation with Josh. "Water under the bridge."

Ida asked, "Are you going to see him again?"

Sarah shook her head and confessed, "He wants me to go to the movies with him."

"And?" Ida said.

"Do you know what?" Sarah said. "It's too silly."

"Why?" Ida asked.

"Because," Sarah said and could not be persuaded to say more.

The next day, when Josh phoned despite her rejection of his offer and again invited her to the movies, Sarah surprised herself and agreed.

She could not explain it to her sister.

The next week, they did it again.

Sarah said to Ida, "Don't ask. I don't understand myself. We have a nice time, but it's nothing like when we were young." She added, "It's just something that I think I owe myself."

Ida agreed and kissed her.

Then Sarah decided to stop seeing him. "All these years. Too much has happened," she said.

"Not enough has happened," Ida suggested.

"That's true too," Sarah said. "You're smart. Maybe I can't stand to think about it."

They were silent. Ida said, "That sounds right."

Sarah said, "I've lived my life as well as I could."

"I know."

"I taught myself what I could hope for. And what not to want."

"I know."

"Why stir things up?"

"No reason," Ida agreed. "Except . . ."

"No," Sarah said. "What's the good of it?"

"A little company, a nice guy. Why not?"

Sarah shook her head. "No. There are some feelings, Ida, that I am not going to touch. And that's that."

When Ida looked dismayed, Sarah shook her head again. And this time, she did not change her mind.

Part Six:
Ida and Abe

1. How Long Has This Been Going On?

Ida had found a table for Sarah and herself near a big window with a view of the lawn and shrubs and of the changing seasons for those who wanted to look. The sisters did. And since they were two at a table for four, Millie, the tall, blond hostess, sat the new arrivals, Abe and Helen Hirsch, with them. Abe was an amputee in a wheelchair; what remained of his right leg was neatly wrapped and sticking out straight. Ida couldn't look. Helen was amputated too, mentally deteriorated. Abe was taking care of her and not asking anyone for help. He was not the type.

Abe gave Ida the once-over. Her hair had been blond-streaked at the Seven Oaks beauty parlor; she wore makeup and costume jewelry and had a peppy manner. He saw that Sarah was plain and watchful. But Ida seemed like a live one. His wife was failing. and Abe was looking, even with his amputated leg. Why not? He wanted company.

Ida remembered. It had been a while, maybe forty years, but after a few days, she picked up on Abe's interest. The main thing, she sensed, was that he was not looking for a quiet woman. So she challenged him when he complained about their young black waitress. "I told Ruby we need more rolls, and she's not going to do anything about it."

Ida spoke up. "Ruby heard you, mister. She'll bring the rolls. She wants this job. And she doesn't need you to yell at her."

Abe, alert now, looked at Ida who looked back. They both experienced a shock of recognition, like a lightning bolt, like in her romance novels, she told herself. He laughed out loud. She blushed and realized that she was having a hard time not smiling at him. "Lord," Ida told herself. "It's been so long."

The others saw. Sarah drew a sharp breath. Helen knocked over her water glass. Ruby brought napkins to cover the wet tablecloth. She dumped rolls into the breadbasket. She was no pushover.

Ida frowned. *What have I done? I must have lost my mind. I need a boyfriend like a hole in the head.*

Sarah thought, *Now I've seen everything.*

Abe was pleased. *He wanted a little spice in his life.*

Ida was pleased too. *Some things you just don't forget.*

As they all left the dining room, the sisters watched Abe push ahead in his wheelchair, dragging along Helen. Sarah grabbed Ida's arm. "What do you think you're doing with that man? Do you have any idea how that looks?"

Ida had never worried about the consequences of flirtation. Now, she saw herself on the verge of a courtship like in the old days. Even better than the old days. She realized that here she could flirt by day and have her nights to herself.

By day, while Helen napped, Ida and Abe had time together. They told each other about their past lives and discovered they both had been born on the same day on Kirby Street, but a block away and had never met. "We've lived parallel lives," Abe commented.

They talked carefully about their spouses.

"Helen and I were close," he said quietly. "She still needs me."

They were quiet, thinking about Helen.

Ida said, "Darn it." Then she said, "Charlie was good to me."

"What does that mean?"

Fair question, she admitted to herself and did not know how to answer him. She was not going to discuss her marriage with a stranger. But recent nights in her apartment, calmed by her pills, it had dawned on her that in all those years, she and Charlie never challenged one another. As a widow in one of her romance novels admitted, "Pierce and I chose the paths of least resistance." This rang a bell for Ida who remembered many evenings in her bed reading, watching game shows on TV and being sedated while Charlie watched sports on TV in his separate bedroom. *That was terrible, Charlie,* she thought. *And we were both responsible.*

Much in the last years was foggy, but summoning up this history as much as she could was freeing for her, and she began to relish a feeling of liberation. In her gang, as far as she knew, couples avoided confrontations. But buoyed now by this feeling about herself, she wanted clarity. In the residents' lounge, after lunch, she looked Abe right in the eyes. "What do you expect from me?"

Abe had an answer to everything. "Closeness." He liked to act out his statements. He leaned over to her, way out of his wheelchair. "I need a woman. You need a man."

She laughed. "You're smug. That bothers me."

"What are you talking about?"

She punched him on the shoulder. "You take me for granted. You shouldn't."

They smiled at each other. Breathing deeply, Ida wondered if he was feeling what she was feeling. "Are you surprised?"

"At what?"

"Surprised at what's happening. Surprised at this?"

He laughed. "Not at all. It's fate. Right?"

She punched him again. "You must be surprised."

He confessed. "Of course I am. But do you know what?"

She made a sound like a cat and settled back into her chair. "What, Abe?"

"This is rare," he told her. "And we don't have much time. So I'm not going to play games."

"That's okay with me," she told him.

"Okay then," he said. "That's that."

Ida wondered, *How long has this been going on?* She realized that she was remembering a lyric from a Gershwin song she used to love.

I could cry salty tears.
Where have I been all these years?
Is it fun? Or should I run?
How long has this been going on?

Life hasn't changed all that much, she thought. Like the old-time music she could still hear on the radio, "It's been going on all these years; it will always go on." She had an impulse to share this realization with Sarah, but decided against it. Ida shook her head. "Sarah never has understood about romance. It always has been that way with us."

2. Abe's Turn

Abe had been cited for speeding in his wheelchair through the long, cream-colored corridors of Seven Oaks. The head social worker, Mrs. Rhea Feldstein, defended him in a meeting to which Abe had been summoned.

"Mr. Hirsch is experiencing a great deal of tension because of his wife's serious health problem," she told the assistant director, Mrs. Lois Smithers, and her boss, Mr. Walter Flowers, also black.

Abe, in his wheelchair, his amputated leg sticking into the room like an accusation, was studying the three of them and didn't like what he saw. At best, he was wary with blacks, and he did not care for women like Mrs. Feldstein. He had often dealt with smart, talkative females in his butcher shop and had labeled her as another too-good-to-be-true.

Mr. Flowers, who was impatient because he believed that this matter was beneath his dignity, wasn't buying the sick-wife excuse. "Mrs. Feldstein, name me a resident who doesn't have a health problem at Seven Oaks."

Mrs. Smithers amplified this view. "Mrs. Hirsch's problem is upsetting, but I'm afraid that it is not a license for recklessness and endangering other residents."

Abe looked pensive and said nothing.

Mr. Flowers tried for a confidential man-to-man approach. "My friend, please understand. We are concerned that one of our less agile residents may not be able to dodge your wheelchair. Why don't you use crutches like the other amputees?"

Abe was not interested. "I don't like crutches."

Mrs. Smithers chipped in. "They can't hear you approaching from behind, Mr. Hirsch. Someone is going to get hurt. And Seven Oaks could be sued."

Abe now understood that he had nothing to fear from these people. They were not going to throw him out of the facility, and they could not ground him by taking away his wheelchair. "I know what I'm doing," he told them. "You don't have to worry."

"I am not reassured, Mr. Hirsch," Mr. Flowers said. "We need you to slow down a bit. Will you do that for us?"

Abe frowned, looked straight ahead and did not speak.

"I'm sure that he will do that for us," Mrs. Feldstein said. "Isn't that right, Mr. Hirsch?"

Finally, Abe said, "I already said that you don't have to worry." And he turned and wheeled rapidly out of the office.

The others stared at the door. Mr. Flowers shrugged. "He's crazy as a loon."

Mrs. Feldstein said, "I don't know why, but I like him."

Mrs. Smithers was not happy. "Have you watched him dashing down the halls in that wheelchair?"

"Greased lightning," Mr. Flowers agreed. "I've never seen anything like it."

From: Abe Hirsch
To: Jake Herman
Re: Report from the zoo

Jake: This place is loony tunes. They hauled me into the director's office because they think I go too fast in my wheelchair. Can you believe it? Do they think I'm going to creep along like the rest of these old farts?

I told them not to worry, but what they didn't know was that I had already hit somebody, a fuzzy-minded guy who falls a lot. He turned the wrong way when I was coming up behind, and I clipped him. He never saw me. I turned around and went the other way. There was no one else there or they might have nailed me for hit-and-run, right?

This is what life is like here for me. A word of advice, old pal. Take the pipe before you let them put you into a place like this. I'm not kidding.

Helen is getting worse. She wants to go home. So do I. If only we could, but we can't. So that's that.

It's good to have someone to talk to, to get some of this off my chest.

Stay healthy,
Abe

Helen Hirsch became confused when Ruby, their waitress, asked her if she wanted chicken, salmon or brisket for her main course.

Abe frowned and leaned toward his wife. "Helen, Ruby needs to know what you want to eat."

Helen looked at Abe, hoping that he would answer for her. When she realized that he was not going to, her dark eyes, under a cloud of white hair, darted doelike around the big dining room and lost their animation. She was near crying.

Ida and Sarah squirmed in their chairs, as if unable to find a comfortable position. Abe did not want to have to explain himself, but decided that he had better make the effort.

"You see, it's just that Helen gives up without trying. She needs to try harder, don't you, dear?"

Helen looked alarmed. Abe noted that Ida had opened her mouth, then paused and left her comment unspoken.

Abe had a theory that he thought would fit this situation. "In general, don't you think it's better to let out your feelings?" He looked at them expectantly.

The sisters, not understanding where he was going with this thought, glanced at each other and waited for him to continue.

Abe clinched his argument. "Helen has always kept things in. I'm thinking that that's maybe why she developed," he glanced at this wife, "her problem."

Abe drummed the table and waited for a comment.

Ida helped him out. "It's very difficult, we understand."

Sarah added, "Yes, it's very difficult."

Given this reprieve, Abe tried one more time with Helen. "Honey, listen to me. Chicken, salmon or brisket. Which one do you want?"

He had tried to wring the irritation from his voice, but she twisted her napkin and her mouth and did not respond.

He willed her to reply. "Helen . . ."

She drew in a deep breath. "Brisket?"

Ida decided it would be helpful to applaud her effort. "Good for you, Helen."

Abe looked surprised and frowned. He did not want the others involved.

Helen became expansive. "I happen to love brisket."

Abe couldn't help saying, "So why don't you remember it?"

Helen faded again.

They ordered brisket, with Abe speaking for Helen who was afraid of Ruby. Then he muttered, "I can't believe I've ended up like this."

The sisters understood. Here was this big man in a wheelchair with his right leg amputated above the knee and having to care for a wife who before their eyes was sliding into dementia.

Helen looked at Abe and the sisters. She opened her mouth as if to speak. They waited. Abe could see by her eyes that she was having one of her lucid moments. "Oh, Abe," she whispered. "I'm so sorry, Abe."

From: Abe Hirsch
To: Jake Herman
Re: Report from the Land of the Coo coos.

Jake: I hate to say it, but Helen is in La-La land. She knows who I am once in a while, and that's about it.

And listen: this place is filled with randy old women. They make goo-goo eyes at me, can you believe it? Me with my one leg. As if I could jump out of my wheelchair and hump them. What the hell, maybe I should try it.

Do you ever go by my butcher shop? Have you been to the ballgame? I watch the games on TV. And I visit the Tigers web site. Jake, what would I do without my computer?

Take care.
Abe

Ruby deliberately mixed up orders. Abe, who believed that systems should work and that people should do their jobs, was grim when she showed up with two eggplant parms and two roast chickens. "We ordered three eggplants and one chicken."

Ruby, calmly and with all the time in the world, consulted the order she had written on her pad. "That's not what it says here, mister."

A flush mounted from Abe's neck to the top of his bald head. "Then why don't you write down what we tell you?"

They glared at each other. Ida squeezed Abe's hand. "You're upsetting Helen," she told him. "Don't let Ruby get your goat. She's doing it on purpose. She wants you to lose your temper."

Abe looked at Ida. "Are you serious?"

"Look at her," she told him.

Ruby was grinning. Abe drew a deep breath. "I see. I underestimated you."

She shrugged. "You're not the first one. I'm just a dumb colored girl, right?"

Abe smiled now. "I guess not."

Ida and Sarah were amazed. Without warning, Ruby had become a person. She picked up a plate of chicken. "I'll change this for an eggplant." She walked away, her hips swinging.

Abe said, "Who needs this?"

Ida laughed. "Ruby plays games."

"What a place," he said. "The residents are demented, and the help is nuts."

From Abe Hirsch
To Jake Herman
Re: Joining the crazies

Jake: Some days I don't know whether to laugh or cry. Ruby, our waitress, brings me anything, but what I order. If I ask for chicken soup, she brings cranberry juice. Salmon turns into beef stew. Instead of apple pie, I get fruit cup. What can I do? I eat the fruit cup and say, "Hey, that's good apple pie." Ruby laughs. The sisters laugh. I laugh. Why not? I've joined the crazies.

Also, yesterday, I'm cruising in my wheelchair, and I turn a corner, and there, right in my way, is the director, Mr. Flowers. He was quick on his feet. You could call it a near miss. "Sorry," I said. "I'm late for arts and crafts." He was not happy.

Take care,
Abe

Ruby, as usual, was enjoying herself. "Three kinds of Salisbury steak. Rare, medium or well-done. Don't matter what you order, you'll get what they give you."

Abe, who for most of his working life owned a kosher butcher shop, could not tolerate the poor quality of hamburger that Seven Oaks called Salisbury steak. And he did not care for Ruby's idea of a joke.

"Spare us the attitude, will you?"

Ruby pulled out her pad. "Soup or salad," she said to Helen, who cringed.

Abe had told Ruby over and over not to talk to Helen. He pushed his wheelchair from the table. "I'm going to the manager," he said and headed for the kitchen.

Ruby shrugged and turned to the sisters.

"Salad with French dressing, Ruby dear," Ida said. She felt like a traitor to Abe, but was in the habit of obeying the staff at Seven Oaks.

Ruby glanced at Sarah who told her the same.

"I'll get it for missus too," Ruby said, not bothering to look at Helen. She followed Abe to the kitchen and arrived in time to watch the end of a shouting match between Abe and Mrs. Walsh, the food manager, who was not interested in his complaint about Ruby's offhand manner.

"Comes with the territory, mister." Mrs. Walsh was bending over the soup kettle. "Get used to it."

"It's bad enough we have to eat your garbage," he told her. "We don't have to swallow insults from the waitress."

"What insults?" Ruby butted in.

"I don't need any more of your lip, lady."

Ruby was always ready for a fight. "And I don't need your racist remarks, mister."

"What the hell are you talking about?" Abe yelled.

"Shut up, both of you." Mrs. Walsh confronted Abe. "No one is forced to eat here. If you don't like it, you can cook for yourself in your apartment."

"Good idea," he said. "At least I'll know what's in the soup." He wheeled back to his table, grabbed his wife's hand and pulled her out of the dining room with Helen lagging and trying to pull her hand free, but not succeeding. Ida and Sarah watched them vanish out of the door.

"Now what?" Ida groaned.

Ruby arrived with their salads. "Says he's going to do his own cooking."

"He'll never last," Sarah predicted.

Ruby agreed. "You got that right."

Abe had no appetite for making anything other than hamburgers or hot dogs, baked potatoes and head lettuce salad with French dressing from the bottle. Helen had zero interest in swallowing more than two bites.

Because of the silence that had overcome Helen, he had gotten into the habit of talking to her as if she could understand. "Helen, do you know what? I'm thinking about the old days. When we used to go dancing at the Greystone. And you would be wearing that short black dress and your pretty beads. And your dancing shoes, the ones with the heels. And your hair would swing. And I'm in my gray suit, wearing my red tie and the dark gray shirt you said made me look like a gangster. The music was so great and us dancing the whole night. Come on, Helen, come here, sit on my lap. Yeah. 'At's a girl. Here we go. 'Pardon me, boy, is that the *Chattanooga Choo-Choo?*' No, Helen, don't get up. Okay, okay. You can go back to your television. Oh, God."

After a week, they returned to their table in the dining room.

Sarah said, "You lasted longer than I thought you would."

"Home cooking isn't what it used to be," he confessed.

"What is?" Sarah said.

"Nothing much." He looked at Ida. "How're you doing?"

Ida said, "It must have been lonely, just the two of you. At least here you have company."

"Someone to argue with," Sarah said.

"I even missed Ruby," Abe confessed.

"I heard that." Ruby was standing right behind him.

Abe swiveled in his chair to face her. "I didn't mean it."

"Too late," she cackled. "Soup or salad, everyone?"

Mrs. Feldstein reported to Mr. Flowers and Mrs. Smithers. "Mr. Hirsch is adjusting nicely."

Mr. Flowers was surprised. "Has he slowed up? I haven't noticed."

Mrs. Smithers was dismissive. "We haven't seen any adjustment, Mrs. Feldstein."

Mrs. Feldstein, who was a licensed clinical social worker, did not like to have her evaluations challenged. "Give him time," she insisted. "Mr. Hirsch will become a model citizen of Seven Oaks."

Mr. Flowers said, "We can't hold our breath waiting for that, can we?"

Mrs. Smithers said, "We need leverage."

"True," Mr. Flowers said. "And in that regard, I was thinking about Mrs. Hirsch who is severely demented, am I right?"

Mrs. Smithers saw what was coming and smiled. "Oh, yes, severely."

"We should consider the third floor for her, Mrs. Feldstein."

"But, Mr. Flowers," she objected, "Mr. Hirsch is caring for her. They're used to each other."

"Precisely," Mr. Flowers nodded.

Mrs. Smithers beamed at him and spelled it out for Mrs. Feldstein. "We'll make a deal with Mr. Hirsch."

"Slow up or else," Mr. Flowers said.

Mrs. Feldstein was shocked. "That's unfair."

"Not at all. It's for the good of the other residents." Mr. Flowers was ready for the next topic.

From: Abe Hirsch
To: Jake Herman
Re: How it is

Jake, in a few days I am scheduled to meet with the head social worker, Mrs. Feldstein. It will be six weeks since we arrived. The idea is to talk about how I am adjusting.

She told me that it would be helpful if I made a list of things I miss from my old life, plus the reasons why I came here, and also some things that are bothering me now. So I made up a scorecard:

Things that I miss:

Having Helen cook my dinner and just the two of us eating in our dining room. Also eating when we feel like it, not when a bell rings.

My car. (You can't believe how I miss having my own car, taking care of it, washing it, changing the oil.)

Going to the movies with Helen.

Taking her dancing.

The birds in our garden and the bird feeder. (Helen must miss the garden if she thinks about it.)

Sharing a scotch on the rocks before dinner. I have a bottle in our apartment here. It's no fun by myself, but usually I need a drink or two.

Here is what I don't miss (why I came here):

Having to clean the house myself.

Having to make sure that Helen doesn't hurt herself in the kitchen or wander down the block or invite strangers into our home.

Being alone with Helen 24/7.

Watching her lose her mind and nobody to help or talk to.

Finally, here is the grief that moved here with me:

Helping Helen dress, cleaning her up when she makes a mess.

Seeing the look on her face when she understands for a moment what is happening to her.

Not minding that she is going to die soon. It will be a relief.

Jake, I won't tell the social worker all this. I'm sure she's heard it before. In fact, I'm not even going to e-mail it to you.

> Keep the faith.
> Abe

Abe and Mrs. Feldstein were wary. "Mr. Hirsch, it's usually difficult at Seven Oaks for people who have been independent all of their lives."

Abe nodded. "It's a big change."

"But you're getting used to it?" she probed.

"Yeah, sure."

Mrs. Feldstein hoped that Abe had made a few friends.

Abe said that he had. "Why not? We're all in the same boat, right?"

She agreed. "There are good people here. I hope you'll give them a chance. Seven Oaks can make these retirement years a real pleasure."

"Yeah, right," he murmured.

Mrs. Feldstein got to the point. "How is Mrs. Hirsch feeling, Mr. Hirsch?"

Something in her voice alerted him. "She's okay. We're managing."

She sounded thoughtful. "Mr. Flowers and Mrs. Smithers actually think she might do better on the third floor."

Abe struggled to swallow his rage. "Oh?"

"The thing is, Mr. Hirsch, that I might just be able to talk them out of it."

"Oh?"

Mrs. Feldstein was uncomfortable. "I know that if you slowed down a bit on your wheelchair, they might be willing to reconsider."

That was as much as Abe could take. "Yeah," he murmured. "I get it." He wheeled out of her office at his usual speedy pace.

Mrs. Feldstein was giddy with guilt, relief and doubt. Later, to her husband, she confided, "We have this resident in a wheelchair. He has such a strong personality. You want him to like you."

From: Abe Hirsch
To: Jake Herman
Re: Escape

Dear Jake: They are closing in on me, buddy. I know why. I don't conform. I'm the only one in this whole zoo who goes his own way, and the keepers can't stand it. They are slowing me up, and they even want to shift the waitress I was having fun with. I think the people at the next table complained that she was spending too much time on us.

I guess you're not supposed to like it here.

Jake, I hope that when Helen dies I have enough spirit for me to leave this place. Do you think you could put me up for a few days?

> Your old buddy,
> Abe

3. Bingo

Abe was in the bingo room watching the game. A-7, G-52, O-74. The tension of the players reminded him of Las Vegas. Hunched over, residents glanced furtively at their neighbors' cards and uttered groans of dismay or small cheers of victory. He never played. He hated the idea of waiting for a number to be called and slowly filling out a card with an ink marker.

Years ago, Abe wanted to enjoy life, which included having fun with Helen before her Alzheimer's dementia set in. He treated them to trips to Las Vegas, even though he was already amputated and in his wheelchair. He played blackjack, poker and craps while Helen fell into a trance pushing buttons on the slot machines for hours at a time. He gambled with five, ten or twenty dollar chips, depending on how his cards were running. She played the quarter machines, and if she were ahead, which happened now and then, tried the dollar slots. They each had a limit on how much they were willing to lose and tried to manage their money so that it would last for at least three or four hours into the night. Later, in bed, they recounted their wins and losses and laughed.

But at Seven Oaks, memories of those nights left Abe feeling frustrated. He was vigorous and could have gone back to Vegas and competed with big shots. What the hell was he doing in this bingo room anyway, with empty-headed people marking little boxes with their felt pens as if it mattered, as if their lives depended on the utterances of a woman calling numbers?

In addition, he had a notion that he knew was a little nuts: maybe one day he would go back to Las Vegas with Ida who, at this moment, was laying out six fresh bingo cards. He could almost hear Helen mocking him. "Oh, Abe! What's the matter with you?" And as usual she would have been right. *Pretty crazy*, he thought, *but what the hell.*

He and Ida had known each other for three weeks. If she had divined what he was thinking, she would, no doubt, have walked away as fast as she could. Well, it was his private plan, and he was going to play it close to the vest. Abe knew that Seven Oaks was a terminus for the people around him, not a way station. One thing for sure, he had no intension of spending the rest of his life in this place.

In fact, Ida had seen Abe in the room and was annoyed. She didn't want him to spy on her and ruin her fun. She liked the bingo evenings, especially the intervals between games when they gossiped and laughed. What could be better than sitting next to Sarah and listening to their pal, Miriam, tell stories?

This one was about Jean Green, Ida's purple-haired enemy who was at the next table. Miriam had a confidential way of talking in which her lips barely moved, and her eyes darted between Ida and Sarah. Miriam's opening remark captivated them. She said that years ago, Jean Green's husband had left her to marry her own sister.

"Really!" Ida was delighted. "Who ever heard of such a thing?"

Sarah said, "I don't think that's so surprising."

Ida threw her a look. Both of them thought about Charlie and his long, close friendship with Sarah, who also remembered that the only thing that Charlie had ever wanted was to complain about Ida.

Miriam wasn't finished. "Wait, a year after her husband left Jean for the sister, he turned around and went to live with a rich shiksa."

"Oh, my God," Ida said. "He was a crazy man."

"There's more," Miriam said. "The shiksa was a relative of Henry Ford, though distant."

Ida wondered how Jean's ex could have met a relative of Henry Ford when Mrs. Smithers, who was calling the numbers, announced that the game was about to resume.

The room went silent; players hunched over their blank cards, ink daubers poised. "Come on," Ida muttered. She hadn't had a bingo all night and made a last-minute plea to Charlie for divine intervention. Sarah made a sign with her fingers that their mother once promised would bring good luck. Mrs. Smithers intoned, "B-4." Ink daubers squeaked. A few residents grunted in satisfaction, others groaned, including the sisters and Miriam.

Then just like that, Ida had a bingo on the next seven calls and shouted, "Okay! I got it!"

"Let's see your card, please." A staff person called out Ida's ink daubs to Mrs. Smithers who read the numbers.

Validated, Ida crowed, "That's more like it." She went to the head table to collect her ten dollars and headed for the door.

"Hold it, lady." It was Abe, bulky in his wheelchair.

"Fancy meeting you here." Ida could feel her heart beating.

"I know," Abe said. "I played when I was ten years old. We used little wooden disks then."

"They've had daubers for twenty years." She teased him. "It's not so terrible. Why don't you try it?"

"Oh, Lord." He shook his head.

And truly, Ida could not visualize Abe, who had more energy than he knew what to do with, sitting still for an evening of bingo. She had watched him careening on his wheelchair through the corridors of Seven Oaks and had had the recurring sense that he was yearning to roll right out the front door, leaving behind this world of the tame, the sedentary and the dim-minded, not to mention his poor wife.

As she left the room, Abe moved alongside. He put his hand on her shoulder. They looked at each other. "So?" she said.

"It feels right to me," he told her.

She shook her finger at him. "We'll see."

He laughed. "I came by to see if we could talk a little." When she looked hesitant, he added, "Unless you can't wait to get back to your room."

This was closer to the truth than she liked to think. Her pills and TV were calling. "Nobody's waiting for me in my room," she said. "Let's sit in the lounge."

But now conversation was a little forced, and after ten minutes they broke it off. "I have to get back to her," he said. "See you tomorrow." He squeezed her hand and wheeled away without looking back.

Ida sighed and headed down the corridor to her room. She was unsettled over the way their encounter had ended, but she was looking forward to her night in bed.

The stabbing in her hands had started up, so she took just one of her pain pills while she waited for the inevitable nighttime headache and for the occasional deep pain that arose mysteriously in her abdomen, possibly emanating from one of her organs—her liver? her kidneys?—which might prompt her to take a few more pills.

But this night's ritual was disrupted. She couldn't get Abe out of her mind. She discussed the situation with her dead husband. *He's just a friend, Charlie. We're both lonely. Nothing's going to happen. I mean that way. I'm not interested in that. Are you mad at me? There was never anybody else, Charlie. How could I start up now? Am I right?*

Ida shivered and sat up. This was not something she wanted to think about, ever. Abe had stirred her. She knew he was still manly. But it was impossible. It could never happen. *Never, never, never. I don't have those feelings anymore. I haven't . . . for years.*

Long ago, she had told Charlie, "I can't do it anymore. I don't feel right. After my operation."

"It's okay, sweetheart," he had said. "I understand."

Ida had sensed that he was relieved. A thin, nervous man, Charlie could never mask his feelings. She could tell that he didn't want to do it. Not with her.

Did Charlie have other women? Probably. He would never say it. And he kept giving her nice things, except when she wanted too much.

Confronted by her expenses, Charlie would throw up his arms in despair. It was what he had always done. Early in their marriage, she had wanted him to say no or to fight with her. But that was not Charlie. He did not have it in him to oppose her. He was a good man, she knew, but not a strong man. For the sake of peace in their home, he bribed her with presents, placated her. She put away her disappointment. What else could she do?

When Ida daydreamed about Abe, she realized immediately that he was not like other men at Seven Oaks. He was certainly nothing like Charlie. What was it about Abe? She decided that he resembled the heroes in her romance novels. She believed she could sense that there was something that those authors wrote about, something coiled in him, a force that might be hard to deflect, like the resolve in Craig in *Brief Romance*. But she decided that she could handle Abe. She would enjoy his company. Why not? As long as he didn't disrupt her routine, her TV watching, her mornings in bed, a few pills at night, which she believed now that she could handle. No way was she going to let a man change her life. Not at this late date. Except on her terms. That she was sure of.

Sarah and Miriam consulted and decided to nip Ida's little romance in the bud. "She'll only get hurt," Sarah explained.

"She's completely innocent," Miriam agreed. "We have to protect her against herself."

They cornered Ida. "Break it off with Abe," they began. "How could you start up with a man with a sick wife?"

Ida flushed scarlet. "Back off, sister of mine," she screeched. "And as for you," she stormed at Miriam. "You're some friend. You should be ashamed."

Leaving her accusers staring at each other in confusion, Ida fled to her room and decided to consult with the ever-sympathetic Larry King.

Larry, am I doing anything terrible? I mean really.
Ida, I don't think you're capable of doing anything terrible.
Why can't people understand that? Why do they have to criticize?
People are like that, Ida. You've seen it all your life.
I have, Larry. You are so right. All I'm looking for now is friendship.
Ida, you are absolutely entitled to have some closeness with a nice man.
His sick wife has nothing to do with it, am I right?
Nothing at all. You're entitled. He's entitled.
I wonder if he's coming to the bingo game tonight.
I'll bet he does. He likes you, and my guess is that he'll come.
Don't tell anyone. I hope he does.
Who would I tell, Ida?
I haven't the faintest idea, Larry.

That evening at bingo with Sarah and Miriam, Ida was having trouble following the calls. Miriam told her, "Ida, you have bingo!"

"What! Oh, bingo! I have it!"

Jean Green overheard. In voice that carried throughout the room, she said, "Ida must be in love. She didn't even know she had bingo."

"Terrible woman," Ida said.

But Miriam, for once, had to agree with Jean. "That's what happens when a man comes into your life."

Ida said, "Oh, Miriam, no."

Sarah was angry. "Never mind, she knows what she's talking about."

Ida looked around for Abe. "Maybe he'll come," she murmured. She pushed her cards into a pile and said, "I think I'll sit out the next game." Just then Abe nudged his wheelchair into the room. She waved to him. He waved back. Sarah said, "Now I've seen everything."

Ida laughed. She felt like she was in command of her world. "Honey, you haven't seen anything yet."

Sarah said to Miriam, "Can you believe this?"

"Absolutely not," Miriam responded.

"Believe it," Ida told them. "It's my chance and I'm not going to blow it."

4. The Van to Kroger

The van operated by Seven Oaks was making its weekly trip to the Kroger supermarket. Ida sat next to Miriam who said that she was going to be a hundred years old next Wednesday. Ida, who was almost eighty, believed that she and Miriam were more alert than the average residents at Seven Oaks, allowing, of course, for normal slips in memory. "I thought your birthday was last Wednesday," she said.

"I knew it was a Wednesday," Miriam said with satisfaction.

"So," Ida said, "did your family give you a birthday party?"

Miriam paused to watch the van driver, Abdul, expertly weave around a long eighteen-wheel Kroger truck. "We're going to the same place," she said. "How do you like that?"

Ida asked her again about the party.

Miriam bobbed her head. "Of course, we had a party and everyone was there except my grandson, Dennis. He's mad because I told him I was going to leave him out of my will."

"Where did you go for your party?" Ida was not going to comment on Dennis whom she had heard had something to do with heroin and rarely saw his grandmother.

"We went to Buddy's for pizza," Miriam said. "I happen to love pizza." She turned around in her seat. "I'm going to be a hundred next Wednesday," she told Jean and Doris, both of whom were thin-faced with purple-tinted gray hair swept up on their heads. Ida's hair was a more sensible blond though she had lived most of her life as a raven-haired beauty. Miriam's thin hair was colored a pale blue.

Jean and Doris also knew that Miriam's birthday was last Wednesday. Jean told Miriam that she couldn't have had a birthday last Wednesday and next Wednesday.

Seeing no problem in this, Miriam told them that she had promised her family that she would live to a hundred and five.

Doris said that Florence Gold had died recently at a hundred and four years old.

"It all depends on how you're feeling," Jean said.

"I'm feeling fine," Miriam said.

"Most of us aren't feeling fine," Jean responded.

"And we don't have her energy either," Ida told them.

Abdul, a slight middle-aged man (not an ounce of fat on him, the women liked to say), was listening and unexpectedly told his passengers that in his country, his grandmother, Allah be praised, was approaching one hundred years of blessed life.

"When is her birthday?" Ida asked.

"In the summer," Abdul said. "The entire village will celebrate. There will be roasted sheep."

"Will you go back to your country for her birthday?" Miriam asked.

"Yes, I am saving my money. I will partake of the sheep at my grandmother's side."

"Do you have a family here?" Ida said. She realized that she was asking a personal question of Abdul who had been driving the van for months and to whom neither she nor anyone else had ever spoken about anything other than their own requests.

"Allah has blessed me," said Abdul. "I have a loving wife and six children. My wife and I miss our families," he added, "but we now are good Americans, praise Allah." He honked at a car that was hesitating between lanes. "She endangers us," he murmured.

"Six children," Ida said. "Isn't that wonderful?"

"Five are boys," Abdul said. "Only one girl who also I love."

"You should bring them to Seven Oaks," Miriam said, "so we can meet them."

Ida laughed. "Yes, Abdul, bring them."

Jean and Doris exchanged alarmed glances. Miriam was capable of saying anything, but what was Ida thinking? Jean whispered to Doris that Abdul would never bring his family to Seven Oaks. It was a ridiculous idea. But Abdul said, "Thank you for your wonderful thought. I consider you all to be my friends, and I would rejoice for you to meet my family."

As he drove into the Kroger parking lot, he honked the horn three times for happiness.

The shopping cart was sturdy to lean on for Ida who had gained some unneeded weight due to her habit of marking the half hours of the nights with chocolate-covered cookies. Hunched over, she steered for the paper products and pulled six rolls of Bounty paper towels off the shelves and eight boxes of Kleenex tissues that were on sale. She bought Bounty because the paper was sturdy and made helpful liners inside of her protective undergarments; she used a lot of tissue because her nose ran all the time.

Ida felt dizzy and leaned over, waiting for her head to clear and her breathing to slow. She was in this position when a male voice said, "Can I help you, Mrs. Nollman?"

Ida looked up at a tall, young, black man, an employee who was smiling at her surprise. "You don't know who I am, do you?"

"I don't think so." How could she possibly know who this was? How could this young black man know her name? Was he a relative of one of the workers at Seven Oaks? Or even of one of the new black residents?

"I'm Perry Brown," he said. Something stirred in Ida's mind, but she couldn't summon it up. "My family rented your mother's house on Kirby Street a long time ago. After the war, we bought the house from her. We still live there. My grandmother and I were at your mother's funeral. It doesn't seem that long ago, does it?"

"Mama," she murmured.

"Nana told me that your mother was a wonderful lady, very kind to our family."

Ida remembered. It must have been fifty years ago that the Browns had rented the house. Perry could not have been born yet. During the war, the family had worked at the Chrysler plant that made tanks for the army in three eight-hour shifts. Along with so many in Detroit, they had done well, and that was how they could afford to buy the house.

Before that, Ida had driven her mother to collect the rent, and her mother made her stay in the car with the doors locked and the windows rolled up. Ida felt foolish watching her vanish into the house. But her mother had said, "They wouldn't hurt an old lady." And actually, Ida had been relieved. Who knew what these colored people were like? Who knew if a pretty, young, white woman would have been safe in that house? Silly, she had told herself. But she had waited and wondered what she should do if her mother did not return.

Now this young man had stepped out of the past like a character in one of her romance novels and was smiling and expecting her to speak.

"Is your grandmother well?" she said. Perry hadn't mentioned his parents, and she wondered what had happened to them. She had heard on television talk shows about black grandparents having to raise their grandchildren. And, in fact, she realized that his parents would have to be her son Freddie's age. So his grandmother would be her generation. She shook her head. Too much.

"Grandma is good," Perry said. "How are you doing?"

"Okay, okay." She smiled vaguely. "Time does fly, doesn't it?"

She wanted to move on, but his hand was on her shopping cart, and he had more to say. "My grandma said that your momma was a fine woman. When times were hard before the war, your momma was patient about the rent. And she used to bring clothes, stuff for grandma and her sisters that you and your sister were done with."

This was embarrassing. Ida could hear her mother. "No money again. Shvartzes. They spend it on schnapps, and they play the numbers. He gets drunk and beats her. They're no good." And picking up a pile of old clothes, "They can have these shmates."

"She was a generous person," Perry said.

"I should kick them out," her mother had said many times. "You can't trust them. And they don't want to work."

"I'm a little dizzy," Ida told him.

"Wait," he said. He ran down an aisle and came back with a stool. "Rest on this, Mrs. Nollman. You shouldn't be here on your own. It must be hard for you."

More than the surprise of encountering him in the Kroger market, she was impressed with his confidence and good looks. He had an air of authority. She asked coyly, "So you work here at Kroger?"

He smiled. "I'm the new assistant manager, Mrs. Nollman."

She sighed. "I'm not used to it."

He knew what she meant. "To African Americans advancing?"

She hung her head. Replaying this exchange in her mind, Ida stood and reached for the cart. "I'm feeling better," she said. "Thank you, Perry. This was a big surprise. Wait until I tell my sister, Sarah. Please say hello to your grandmother for me."

He walked alongside. "I'll tell Nana," he said. "She'll be glad to know we met here. Maybe you and she can get together and talk about old times. I think she'd like that."

He left Ida whose mind was jumping now between her unexpected memories and the always-anxious task of navigating the checkout. When she had trouble counting the money for her purchases, the overweight young black checkout girl took Ida's purse, took out her credit card, swiped it, showed Ida where to sign and put the card back into her purse.

Ida pushed the cart toward the exit. She confided in her dead husband, *Charlie, some of them are nice to me. Too bad she's so fat. A lot of them are fat.* The smiling Abdul was there to help her to the van.

Driving back to Seven Oaks, Ida continued her comments. *Charlie, do you remember the shvartzes that lived in Ma's house on Kirby Street, and they bought it from her after the war? I met the grandson . . . Larry, Harry . . . like that, I can't remember. What's the difference? Perry . . . So he's the manager of Kroger. How do you like that? And he knew me. From Ma's funeral. In a million years I wouldn't have known him. And he wants me to meet his grandmother. Can you beat that? Why would I want to talk with her? About what? The old days? I don't need to remember the old days. Maybe I won't see him again. Why couldn't he let me alone? Who needs this?*

Waiting for dinner with her sister at the entrance to the dining room, Ida described the encounter with Perry and said, "So who needs it? I don't need this."

Sarah could not understand what her sister was so worked up about. "Why are you aggravated? What's the difference?"

"You know I'm not a prejudiced person."

Sarah was watching the dining room entrance. "They opened the door." She kept pace with her sister who moved slowly. It was difficult for Ida to walk and talk. But she gasped, "Am I a prejudiced person?"

Sarah couldn't resist. "If you're not, what are you making such a fuss about?"

"Never mind," Ida muttered.

"You brought it up," Sarah said airily.

At their table with Abe and Helen, Ida realized that after only a few weeks she was barely aware of Abe's amputated leg that was sticking out over the edge of his wheelchair. *It shows how you can get used to anything,* she thought.

Abe was talking in a low voice about the new black residents at a table near them. "You can't escape them."

"What do you mean?" Sarah said.

Abe reached over to help Helen by cutting her lettuce into small pieces. She had been daydreaming and singing "Row, Row, Row Your Boat" in her off-key, little-girl voice.

He said, "Wherever we move, they follow us. It's the history of this city."

"What's the difference," Ida said. "Who cares?" She did not want to be talking about black people because she wanted to forget about Perry Brown. She wanted to change the subject, but didn't know how to accomplish that without sounding out of step with the others. She finally said, "This is America, isn't it?"

Sarah and Abe stared at her. Then Helen said, "Row, row, Abe, how many rows are there?"

"Three," Abe told her. "Say row three times."

Helen did that and felt proud. "I did it!"

"Where were we?" Abe said.

"Racial history in Detroit," Sarah said.

"They used to come into my shop," he told them. "They wanted kosher meat, especially the chicken."

Ida squirmed in her chair and decided to establish her complete lack of prejudice. "Weren't they entitled?"

Abe glared at her. "They knew damn well I didn't want them in my place."

Ida did not want to get into an argument with Abe who seemed to have strong opinions. But she did not like where Abe was headed. She said, "So? What was so terrible, Abe? I mean really."

"Would you go where you weren't welcome?" Abe demanded.

Sarah chipped in. "I might. I would want the best meat for my family."

Ida sided with her sister. "You didn't want them, but you still served them."

Abe threw up his hands. "What? Did I need to be picketed? Did I need a demonstration? You know what they're like."

He looked around and realized that their quiet conversation had escalated in volume to the point where black residents at a nearby table, as well as Ruby, their black waitress who had just arrived, could hear perfectly well what they were discussing.

Abe gazed at Ruby who was standing stock-still behind Helen, her tray of soup bowls balanced on her hip.

Helen, dimly aware that a drama was being enacted, was twisting her napkin. Ruby seemed frozen to the floor, not a muscle moving.

Abe quietly said, "What are you going to do with that soup?"

"Nothing," Ruby said.

"The soup is getting cold," he said.

"So?" Ruby sounded ominous.

"So serve it."

She blinked, but did not budge.

Abe turned to Ida and asked in a loud voice, "Did I tell you what happened to the Tigers last night?"

"What?" She was surprised. "What tigers?"

"Not the ones in the jungle," he said. "The baseball Tigers."

"My God," she said. "What happened?"

"Their cleanup hitter won the game in the bottom of the ninth with a home run."

"Oh."

"He happens to be black. We all cheered."

"Oh."

"Serve the soup, Ruby," he said.

And she did, glaring at him.

By eight-thirty, sighing and groaning, Ida was glad to undress, put on her baby blue pajamas with the white lace collar and cuffs and go to her bathroom. Before leaving the bathroom, she turned on the night light. She turned off the lights in the kitchen and living room and, at last, murmuring to herself, arranged her three pillows and slid her legs under the electric blanket, which she switched on.

Everything she needed was within reach: On her blanket, the TV remote, her TV guide and a romance novel; on the floor, next to the bed, her slippers; the switch for her bedside lamp hung down the right side of her bed (the window side of the room).

On the nightstand to her right, a water glass, the Seven Oaks bulletin of events for the coming week, three other romance novels, her telephone and a package of chocolate-covered cookies.

On the floor, in front of the nightstand, a thermos of ice water, more books and an open box of tissues. By morning, used tissues littered the floor.

In the top drawer of the nightstand, her bottles of pills with their easy-open flip tops, her reading glasses in their red leather case, her small green leatherette book with her personal telephone numbers, most of the entries were for dead friends and relatives, and miscellaneous pens and pencils.

She put on her glasses and considered the TV programs she would watch: *Crossfire*, *Nightline* and *Larry King Live*. In a major change from her pre-Seven Oaks life, Ida now believed in keeping up with current events, even sports (which, she knew, would have astonished Charlie). To her son Fred, she bragged, "Most of the people in this place have no idea what's going on the world. All they watch on television is junk. Your mother doesn't happen to be that kind of person."

She thought about her aggravation over the incident with Perry. She knew how to soothe herself and curled up on her side, a favorite position. After Larry King's program, they talked.

Larry, do I have to meet his grandmother? Why do I have to have anything to do with them?

Ida, we're old friends, so I can tell you this. Isn't it time?

I know what you're saying, Larry.

In all fairness, Ida, and I'm appealing to your sense of justice, isn't it their time? Isn't it their turn?

What can I say, Larry?

It's only fair.

You're right, Larry.

We had our turn.

We did.

It's the American way. Am I right?

You're right, Larry. Believe me, I know you're right. I'm the last person to say no to them. But, Larry, why do I have to be involved?? Why me? I'm an old lady.

You're a thinking person, Ida.

So?

So nobody else in the whole Seven Oaks would step forward and do the right thing at a time like this.

You're right. What can I say? I'm not a prejudiced person.

Thank God for people like Ida Nollman, that's what I say.

Thank you, Larry.

Thank you for being you, Ida. Good night.

Whenever she talked with Larry, satisfaction usually provided a bridge to sleep. But this night, even after a Darvocet for her random pain and an Empirin for her restlessness, she was still upset.

Gradually, her attention was diverted back to the TV. After the late, late movie *Spellbound*, which she had already seen twice, she picked up her book and alternated lurid passages with snatches of restless sleep. In the morning, dark pouches shadowed her eyes.

"How can you be so silly?" Sarah had stopped by for a cup of morning coffee. Ida was still in bed and had resorted to using oxygen from the big green tank.

Sarah extended her arms in a gesture of wonder. "Why are you so worked up over this?"

Ida frowned. "I'm not, Sarah."

"Ma used to give them our old clothes."

"That's one thing I don't like. I feel funny about that."

"Don't feel funny. They were glad to get them."

A few days later in the van, Abdul tapped the horn. "Where to, ladies?" And he murmured, "I am the muezzin."

The flock was ready for the game. "A & P," Jean said.

"Farmer Jack's," Doris said.

"Wal-Mart," Miriam said

In a firm voice, Ida said, "Kroger."

There was general applause.

"I agree, Kroger," Abdul said. He drove to the highway and said, "And now, my friends, I have brought you a song from my country." He opened a plastic case and showed them an audiocassette that he pushed into the player. Arabic music filled the van. A female vocalist began to sing in a high-pitched, and to their ears, whiney tone, a wholly unintelligible song. Abdul's passengers were amazed.

The song was not over when they reached the market. Abdul kept the motor running and the tape going until the singer abruptly stopped. He turned to the women. "It is my gift to you, my friends."

Miriam was the only one to think of something to say. "That was very interesting, Abdul."

Abdul was solemn. "It was my sharing with you, ladies."

The women were silent, until Ida said, "What was the song about, Abdul?"

Abdul looked content. "She sang about a mother's love for her children."

"It's the same for all people," Ida said.

"Ah, you understand," he told her.

"And now it's time to go to Kroger," she replied.

"You are correct." Abdul got out and pulled the walkers and wheelchairs from the back of the van. The passengers disembarked.

Before heading off on her own, leaning on the shopping cart, Ida asked Jean and Doris what they thought of the gift.

Doris said, "I hope he doesn't do that again."

Ida was surprised. "Why not?"

Jean said, "If he does, I am going to complain to the management."

Ida said, "Don't get him in trouble. He means well."

"Jean's right," Doris said. "He had no business making us listen to that terrible music."

"Exactly," Jean said.

Ida reached the checkout counter before she saw Perry who was supervising the installation of a large rack of Wise potato chips. Perry saw her, waved briefly and resumed his work. Ida was disappointed over what she took to be his dismissal.

Sarah was not surprised. "I told you that you were making a mountain out of a molehill."

Ida said, "I don't know what you're talking about. It was never a big deal."

Ida did not want to go back to Kroger. But she could not think of an excuse to tell the others. A week later after another bad night, and after her new sleep inducer, Sleepy Beepy, hadn't worked, she resorted to an early morning double dose of Exedrin, Darvon and Restoril. Ida was on the bus but not speaking; her lips and tongue felt thick.

In the store, she pushed her cart through the aisles, keeping an eye out for Perry. She wanted to spot him first and look the other way. *Why do I even care?* Ida leaned lower over the cart. She was having trouble breathing. And now she was shuffling her feet, barely moving. She thought she heard Perry's voice in the next aisle? She straightened up. "Better get going, sister." *Was that my voice?* Ida spurted forward and collided with a cart rounding the corner. A large black man in a black leather jacket and a black wool watch cap was pushing it. A leggy little girl in the child's seat had distracted him, and even though he was not moving fast, his cart shoved back Ida's. To his surprise and hers, she sat on the floor, dazed. The black man, said, "Sorry about that, ma'am," and reached out his hand to her.

Ida stared at the black hand as if it had appeared from nowhere and had no owner.

People were saying, "Let her alone. Let her sit. She might be hurt."

Perry was there, taking charge.

Jean and Doris were there. "Call 911."

"Hang on," Perry said. "Mrs. Nollman, are you okay?"

"She's injured," Doris said. "This man must have knocked her down."

"Not me," the black man said. "I hardly touched her cart."

"Mrs. Nollman, Mrs. Nollman, can you hear me?" Perry saw that Ida's pupils were dilated.

"Oy." *Was that my voice?*

"Would you like some water?" Perry said. "I don't think she needs 911."

Jean and Doris piped out, "She does. She does. She takes pills."

Perry tried to get through to her. "Mrs. Nollman, shall I call 911?"

Ida understood. She did not want 911. She heard Jean and Doris and believed she could handle the pills. "Oy vey iz meir."

"Are you all right, Mrs. Nollman?" Perry was concerned, nicely sympathetic.

Ida smiled at him. "Get that man's license number."

"I didn't do nothing," the black man said.

"It's okay, brother," Perry said. "You be on your way."

"Wait a minute," Jean objected.

The black man was gone.

"Perry?"

"What, Mrs. Nollman?"

"I certainly would like to see your grandmother again. So would my sister, Sarah."

Perry looked troubled. "Actually, Mrs. Nollman, Nana has been a little under the weather. We'll have to postpone your meeting for a bit."

Ida sensed that he was making up an excuse and felt disappointed. "Perry," she said, "life is full of surprises. Please give my best wishes to your grandmother."

"Well," Sarah said afterward. "They thought Ma was their friend. They should have heard what she said about them."

Ida shook her head and told her sister that their mother was the Browns' friend.

"Then why did she say those things, Ida?"

"She couldn't help liking them," Ida said. "But she wouldn't let herself admit that to us. It went against what she thought we should believe."

Sarah stared at her sister. "Ida?"

"What?"

"How do you know things like that?"

"I don't know," Ida said. "People are like that, aren't they?"

"Okay, okay," Sarah said. "You're too much. What's gotten into you?"

Next week, the van's motor was running, but a new driver, Carl, a gangly blond man with tattoos all the way up both arms, was waiting for them.

"Where is Abdul?" Miriam said.

Carl, in the driver's seat, told them, "He's gone."

Ida said, "What do you mean? He wouldn't leave without telling us."

Carl steered the van onto the highway. "Mr. Flowers had to let him go."

"Why?" Miriam was indignant.

Carl shrugged. He told them that he had heard there were complaints.

"Complaints?" Ida murmured. "Who would complain? He was so nice."

Miriam turned in her seat and looked at Jean who looked away. Miriam asked if she had complained about Abdul.

Jean did not answer. But Doris said, "Abdul had a bad attitude. We didn't like him."

Miriam was appalled. "That's so mean. How could you do that?"

Jean glared at her. "I pay my rent here. I have rights."

"Also," Doris said, "he was an Arab. And most of us are Jewish."

"He was a nice man," Ida said. "That was a terrible thing to do."

"He can get another job," Doris said.

"Oh, my God," Miriam yelled. "Stop the van."

"What?" Carl twisted and looked at her.

"Stop. See there," Miriam said. "On the side of the road."

Carl slowed to a creep. Abdul, his wife and their children were standing in a row.

"Oh, no. Oh, no," Miriam cried out.

Ida said, "Carl, stop the van. Stop it."

Carl stopped.

Ida waved to Abdul who solemnly raised one hand and waved back.

Jean said, "This is too much. Let's go."

"No," Ida said. "Open the door."

"What?" Carl was upset. "What's going on?"

"Open the door. Right now," Ida said.

Carl opened the door. Miriam stepped out of the van onto the grassy edge of the highway. Ida followed, holding on to the door for balance. Cars were swerving left to pass the van.

Abdul stepped toward them and gestured to his wife, his five boys and a girl. "This is my wonderful family." His voice sounded strained and high-pitched.

"How do you do?" Miriam shouted. She seemed really pleased.

"We're so happy to meet you," Ida called and waved vigorously to Abdul's wife and children.

Abdul nodded soberly. His wife raised her hand in a tentative greeting. Carl was standing next to Ida. "You have to get back in the van," he said. "They'll fire me too."

Ida waved again and stepped back into the van. Miriam followed. They drove away watching Abdul and his family who now were all waving.

Carl wanted to know what that was all about.

"That poor man," Miriam said.

"I can't believe that happened," Jean said.

"It was ridiculous," Doris said.

"You're both terrible," Miriam told them.

Ida said, "I'm going to miss Abdul." She clutched Miriam's arm. "We can't let them get away with this."

Miriam squeezed Ida's arm in return. "You're right. We have to fight them." She glared at Jean who refused to be intimidated and stared back at her, stony-eyed.

"We'll see Mr. Flowers when we get back," Ida said. "Don't worry. I'm going to give him plenty."

"Good," Miriam said. "Wait until he gets it from us." They both sat back and contemplated the demolition of Mr. Flowers.

A tall, worried-looking black man, Mr. Flowers, gave them no satisfaction. "Company policy," he said after they had denounced the firing of Abdul. "We don't keep people when there are complaints."

"He was doing a good job," Ida protested.

Flowers pursed his lips. "I had no choice."

Miriam was boiling with the injustice of it all. "What about his family?"

"They're not my concern." Flowers arranged papers on his desk. "He shouldn't have upset any of the residents."

"In my day, in my husband's company, there was such a thing as caring about people and their families," Miriam said bleakly. "Apparently that doesn't happen at Seven Oaks."

Flowers stood. "I have a family too, Mrs. Plotnick. And I have work to do. If you don't mind."

Miriam flushed. "This is a terrible place, Mr. Flowers," she announced. "And we're all trapped here."

The two women walked out of his office, passing a secretary who was talking on the phone. Miriam leaned one hand against the wall and slumped to the carpeted floor.

Ida shrieked and couldn't look. The secretary called 911. When they revived Miriam, she said to Ida, "Don't worry. I'm not a hundred and five yet."

Ida said, "Oy gevalt." She couldn't wait to tell Sarah.

5. Self-Medication

All the residents of the Seven Oaks Home for Seniors understood that everyday aches and pains, muscular cramps, neuralgia, headaches, aching joints, GI spasms and backaches, were part of the price tag attached to the accomplishment of old age. Failing eyesight and hearing loss were considered bad luck, like a soldier being wounded in combat. Serious illness, heart disease, stroke, cancer, was awaiting them all; and again, like soldiers in a war, some would succumb. Survivors might grieve, but soon would resume the daily business of living as pain free as possible.

The pharmaceutical industry, in concert with their agents in the medical profession, did not propose to allow old folks to suffer without succor. Science to the rescue. A flood of pain-suppressing and sleep-inducing potions and pills spilled out of the medicine cabinets and bedside drawers at Seven Oaks. Except for a few stoics and masochists, nobody suffered a lonely bed of needless pain.

When she was only forty-two, Ida attempted a high kick and "threw out" her sacroiliac. She had to walk bent over, one hip thrust to the side. Her doctor prescribed bed rest and barbiturates, warning against the potential for addiction. Ida liked the floaty feeling the medication gave her and, simple as that, slipped into the habit of taking pain pills to soothe herself during unhappy times that multiplied as her marriage deteriorated.

Thirty-eight years later and a resident of Seven Oaks, Ida was still taking full advantage of the wondrous advances of pharmaceutical science. There were certain drugs that she had to take, for an eccentric heartbeat, high blood pressure, a sluggish thyroid, an underfunctioning kidney, a low count of her "good" cholesterol and the dizziness that may have been a by-product of her other pills. On top of this, she had her arsenal of pain medication. She saw no point in limiting herself to a prescribed regimen. She took pride in her ability to function normally by day and sedate herself at night. *The best of all possible worlds*, she assured herself.

Her life became even more enjoyable when Abe arrived at Seven Oaks and began to court her. They were side by side in the residents' lounge; he in his wheelchair, his amputated leg sticking out straight. "You and I can be good together," he had said.

Ida had never wanted to be what she called easy. "What about your wife, mister?"

"Helen hasn't been Helen for a long time. I take care of her. But I need to be close to someone. Don't you?"

She flushed and told him to back off.

He took her hand and said that she needed a man.

She pulled her hand back. "All women don't need men."

"Wrong." He was sure of himself. "They do."

They were holding hands again. Ida couldn't believe it. She was afraid to speak, of shattering the moment. He smiled at her. She smiled back. He stroked her hand. She felt like when she was seventeen and flirting. *I still remember,* she thought. *And I can still do this.*

She had to speak. "It's good between us."

"Yes," he agreed. "It's good. But now I've got to get back to Helen." He moved away rapidly in his wheelchair.

Ida couldn't wait to report to her sister Sarah who was disgusted. "Are you crazy? What about his wife?"

Ida flared. "What are you talking about? He just wants to be friends."

Sarah had always been the voice of Ida's conscience. "Holding hands like teenagers. That's 'just friends'?"

Ida couldn't help blushing. "You've been peeking. Mind your business."

"He's not going to put up with a druggie," Sarah told her.

Ida groaned. "You never know. Maybe I'll stop."

Sarah was the realist. "You'll never stop taking your pills, and that's that."

During lunches and dinners, the big dining room was a drug mart. Knowledgeable residents knew all about the advantages and shortfalls of the available agents and, out of curiosity or a need for more impact or less harsh side effects, engaged in a lively exchange, trading up and down according to different potencies.

When the residents couldn't find what they wanted, they went to Lillian Gross, a lively red-headed resident with a loud laugh. A former nurse, Lillian had stores of pills, tablets and capsules. Her business, which she positioned as a service to friends, depended on the fact that almost everybody at Seven Oaks overdosed, and their prescriptions ran out before their insurance kicked in for a refill. Willing to help friends in need, Lillian charged less than the local pharmacies and the Internet outlets. She knew her customers and never provided medicine that caused a serious problem.

Her son, Alfred, who purchased the goods in Canada, replenished Lillian's stock. With his mother's encouragement, he was pursuing multiple careers, including auto theft, accident insurance fraud and dog stealing. The small amount of money he got for the purchase and resale of drugs was barely enough to compensate him for his time, but it was, after all, being done for his mother. And she had the satisfaction of knowing that she was still contributing to the family fortunes.

Ida was one of Lillian's couriers. Moving around the dining room, she took orders, delivered drugs and announced the weekly specials. This week, a 10 percent discount on naproxen, a generic drug that Lillian guaranteed was just as effective as the brand-named Naprosyn (a huge favorite).

Ida was able to help when Abe's wife, Helen, kept him up at night because she couldn't sleep. He said that he would have to call their doctor. Ida shook her head. "Don't be silly. First you have to leave word with his nurse. Maybe he'll get back to you the next day, maybe not. They'll have to call the pharmacy. You'll have to go in the van to sign the insurance and get the pills. That's three days. In two minutes I can cross the room and tell Lillian you need sleeping pills. You'll have them in a few hours."

Abe did not like being part of the Seven Oaks drug culture, but kept his mouth shut.

That afternoon, Ida handed him a bottle of ten-milligram Ambien tablets. Helen's sleep problems were over.

This transaction was followed by another because Abe had read on the Internet about a new treatment for Alzheimer's. The next afternoon, he asked Lillian if she could supply him with Namenda.

She looked at him sharply. "It's not a cure."

He looked grim. "I'm not expecting a cure."

"But it may slow her deterioration. Use it with Aricept."

"I've got Aricept."

She patted his hand. "I'll have the Namenda tomorrow."

Ida was pleased because Abe was now a pill buyer, so he could not be critical of her pill-taking.

Her reasoning would have been sounder if Abe had been buying the pills for himself. That night, on the chance that she would not sleep well, Ida took a bottle of a sleep inducer and two bottles of pain pills from the drawer of her bedside table. She poured water into a glass and swallowed two pills from each bottle. Waiting for the pills to act, she closed her eyes and listened to Jay Leno without looking at the TV picture.

Have I taken my pills? I don't think so.

She took two more pills from each bottle. She watched Leno, expecting sleep. She felt cold and pulled the electric blanket to her chin. Feeling fretful because of what was on her mind, she checked in with her dead husband. *Charlie, I'm sure you're mad at me, right? You were always jealous, even when you had no cause. You know that's true. So now, a little attention from Abe, what's the harm? It's been so long. My God, don't you think I'm entitled? Well, I know it's too much to expect you to be happy for me. Anyway, Charlie, I've decided that if you don't like it, it's just too bad.*

When she was twenty-one and newly married, Ida had had a vision of love and of trusting a man. Now, she knew better. In the zone between reverie and sleep, she laid it out in a one-way conversation with her sister: *Sarah, I never wanted to be telling Charlie what to do. But I didn't want to have to hold him up all the time either, every single day. Sarah, he pulled me down. Where was love? Where was trust? What if I can have them with Abe? Shouldn't I try for that? Even with what's happening with his wife, if he doesn't mind, why should I? I know what you're going to say. He won't trust me if I can't stop taking pills. But what if I can stop? At least stop enough? I'm going to try. Nothing in this world is impossible.*

Ida slept. She had to go to the bathroom. Get up, get up. She moved herself to the edge of the bed, pushed off the cover and swung her feet to the floor. She slowly stood. She was dizzy and sat, her feet dangling over the side. She stood again, holding on to the headboard, closing her eyes against the dizziness. She felt herself leaking. She had to get to the bathroom. Holding the wall, the door to her bedroom and the door to the bathroom, she got to the toilet, sat and dried herself. She stood, sat again, stood and felt for the bathroom door . . .

Morning light. *What time is it? Where am I? In the bathroom. On the floor. Oh, God.* She crawled to the bedroom. *I want to get into my bed.* She couldn't get herself off the floor.

Knocking on the door. Key in the door. Door opening.

"Yes?"

"Ida? You okay?" It was Clara, one of the Seven Oaks staff.

"Yes." *I'm in bed. I got into bed.*

"You sound funny."

"I overslept."

"I'll say. They're going into lunch. They asked me to see if you're okay."

"I'll get up."

"You better. What happened to your eye?"

Ida raised her hand to her face. "My eye?"

"You got some black eye."

"I do?"

"You fall down?"

"I don't know."

"Wait'll your sister sees that."

Ida touched her eye again. It was tender. She could feel that it was swollen. "I'll get up. Thank you, Clara."

Clara bent closer. "Whew. You must have fell and bumped your eye."

Ida got out of bed and swayed. Clara steadied her. "Okay, Clara?" Ida was moving to her closet. "I can do it. Please tell my sister I'm coming to lunch." *Where are my sunglasses?*

In the dining room, Ida walked slowly past tables of chattering residents, some of whom noticed her tentative movements and out-of-place sunglasses and shook their heads. At Seven Oaks, people who were not afflicted at the moment had a survivor's reaction, thankful that it wasn't them, then a rush of hostility toward the victim. Who needed to be reminded of failing health?

predestined by the experience of another woman in another time?

As a last resort, Ida sought Charlie's opinion. Standing in the corridor outside of her door, she was shocked to hear what sounded to her like his spectral laughter.

Absorbed in this out-of-body experience, Ida almost missed the unexpected sight of Mrs. Smithers, the associate director, and Mrs. Feldstein, the head social worker, knocking on Lillian's door.

The next day, she mentioned the incident to Sarah.

"Lillian's making a ton of money," Sarah said. "I'll bet management is getting a cut."

Ida was shocked. "I can't believe that."

"Believe it," Sarah told her. "That's the way the world is."

Ida used Sarah's suspicion as a way of drawing Abe into a conversation. She asked, "Do you think it could be true?"

"Of course," he said. "Your sister is no dummy."

Ida looked at Helen who was listless and staring into space. "How is she doing?"

"Same," he said and added, "you're looking good."

Ida, sensing that she's on a roll now, said, "I'm fine. Take care. I have to meet someone."

She left him leaning forward in his wheelchair, wondering whom she was meeting. She walked away with her heart thumping, pleased with herself.

She told Sarah about the conversation. Her sister was impressed. "I didn't think you had it in you."

Ida said, "You better watch my stuff, baby. It's like old times for Ida."

Sarah laughed. "Now I've heard everything."

"What are you laughing at?" Ida said. "This is the old me."

"Pre-Charlie?"

Ida nodded and touched her sister's shoulder. "Even better. Maybe that and early-Charlie."

Sarah squeezed Ida's hand. "Maybe," she suggested, "you're going back to a better place in your life."

"Maybe." Ida liked the sound of that.

"Why did you start with the pills?"

Ida thought about it. "I don't know. It was a gradual thing. It started a long time ago."

"And now?" Sarah probed. "What about now?"

Ida didn't answer right away. She finally said, "I want to be honest."

"That will be a change," Sarah murmured.

Ida nodded. "I think that I'm not going to go back to what I became." To her surprise, she was weeping. "But how can I know what's going to happen?"

"Ida, that is such an honest statement."

Ida wiped her tears. "We'll see," she said. "Right?"

Sarah squeezed her hand. "That's right, sister. You're absolutely right."

6. Something More

Abe Hirsch awoke in the dark. Next to him, Helen had been thrashing her legs. He put his hand on her shoulder. She turned toward him, trembling. He was uncomfortable. His arm was trapped, but he would not rouse her because their bedroom seen through her confused eyes might have been a more frightening place than the one in her nightmare.

Two years ago he would have touched her breast and wakened her gradually until she bit his ear. He closed his eyes, like hers, an attempt at a kind of communion.

He sighed and briefly allowed the thought that he wished it were over for Helen. He sighed again. Soon enough, and what then? He sat up in bed. He knew he wanted something more in his life.

7. The Hug

The dining room was agreeably dressed for Thanksgiving dinner. Posters taped to the walls portrayed American Indians harvesting maize, lifting pumpkins and chasing turkeys. Six-inch cardboard cutouts of pilgrims armed with muskets and Indians, carrying bows and arrow-filled quivers, greeted one another on each of the thirty or so tables. Small plastic pumpkins filled with tasty little orange and black candies waited at the residents' place settings. Donna, the blond hostess, imposing in bosom and height, was wrapped in a frilly apron entirely fronted by a gobbler; she also wore a white cap meant to approximate the bonnets worn by pilgrim women.

At their table in front of the big picture window, Ida and Sarah were waiting for Abe and Helen. Ida watched him, alone, roll toward them across the dining room and had the sensation, not for the first time, that he had pointed his amputated leg and wheeled where it led him. She was pleased with this odd notion.

Abe looked grim and explained why he had come without Helen whose mind was chaotic with her Alzheimer's disease.

"She has accidents. It's better for her to stay in the apartment. I'll bring her meals now. Not that she eats."

"Oh, Abe," Ida said. "She doesn't know what's happening?" Her tone was confidential; she wanted to show Sarah that she and Abe had moved into a kind of intimacy.

"She's in and out," he said.

Sarah said, "I could sit with Helen if you want some time off, Abe."

He was surprised. "That's nice of you, Sarah. I may take you up on that."

He turned to Ida and covered her hand with his. "We could have a little time together."

A bulky, balding man with powerful shoulders and arms, Abe had a physical presence that all the women at Seven Oaks were aware of. He took up space. He spoke and laughed loudly. His movements were emphatic. When he leaned over in his wheelchair and put his big hand on Ida's, she shivered. So did Sarah who was watching intently.

Ida blushed and pulled her hand from Abe's grasp and hid it in her lap. "He doesn't own me," she murmured. *Coward*, she accused herself.

Neither Abe nor Sarah seemed to have heard. *Did I say that out loud? I thought I said it out loud.* Ida looked at Sarah who was staring at Abe. He was looking intently at Ida. Sarah thought, *I wish he would look at me that way.*

Since Abe had arrived at Seven Oaks, he and Ida had been together during the days: he gave her computer lessons, she was almost hopeless, they sat side by side at weekly sing-ins, and they simply hung out in the lounge and talked aimlessly and endlessly. "We don't have much time," he told her. "We can't waste this opportunity." Meanwhile, his wife's mind was becoming as brittle as a yellowed autumn leaf.

"I'm not going anywhere," she had answered, feeling some satisfaction.

Ruby approached their table. "Guess what? Turkey tonight with fixings. White meat or dark?" She glanced at the empty chair. "Missus ain't eating?"

Abe told her that he would bring Helen's dinner to her. For no apparent reason, he smiled at Ruby, then at Ida and Sarah.

Ruby was taken aback. "White meat or dark?"

They ordered, and Ruby carefully wrote on her pad. Abe reached for Ida's hand again. Ruby rolled her eyes and departed. Ida put her other hand on his hand. Abe followed suit with his free hand. So they were locked together rather awkwardly, but neither wanted to move.

Sarah asked what the doctor had told him.

"Excuse me," Abe said to Ida, as he lifted the cutout of the pilgrim to his ear. He shrugged and set it back on the table. "I get as much information from this guy."

They both took charge of their own hands.

We're like teenagers, Ida thought. "How long does she . . ."

Abe was getting irritated. "Nobody knows. She's going downhill."

Ida sympathized. "After all these years, Abe."

Sarah was sad. "At least you had someone."

Abe looked at her. "You could have."

Sarah put her hand to her cheek as if he had slapped her.

Ida's voice rose. "Abe, really, how can you say such a thing? You hardly know us."

Sarah was grim. "Nobody asked."

"You're a good person, Sarah," he told her. "But you never really wanted to give yourself to a man."

"How do you know that?" Sarah wanted to hit him.

Abe was sure of himself. "I can tell. I know women."

"I was lonely too," she mourned. "I was lonely, and I wanted someone."

"It's not the same," Abe said.

"Ida was the princess," Sarah was testifying now. "She had everything. She traveled. She had nice clothes. She and Charlie joined the country club. She even played golf, the princess."

Abe nodded. "You had different lives. Ida couldn't help it. You couldn't help it. It was the way it was."

Ida turned to Sarah. "I couldn't help it. That's how it was. We were always different. How could two sisters be so different?"

Sarah, who had heard this before from Ida and never had managed a satisfactory response, gave up. "I had to take care of Ma and Pa. What does it matter now? It's water over the dam."

Abe grabbed Ida's hand again. She looked around hoping to signal Ruby, who was, in fact, in the kitchen discussing matters with her friend, Thelma.

"The man is holding her hand," Ruby told her. "Something going on."

"Sex," Thelma offered with a grin.

"Whoa." Ruby burst out laughing.

"You never too old." Thelma nudged her.

"What?" Ruby nudged her back.

"Still some juice in that man," Thelma said.

Ruby was incredulous. "God, can't you see it. Don't want to look at that."

"A sight I don't want to see," Thelma agreed.

"Him with his one leg pumping on one of them dried-up old hens."

"Which one?" Thelma was intrigued by the incongruity of sex among their old-timers.

"That Ida." Ruby laughed. "She the one."

"No juice in her," Thelma said.

"Don't be saying that," Ruby said. "She's the giggly lady."

"I can't think it," Thelma decided.

"Just don't make me watch. Uh uh."

"You have the best table," Thelma said.

Others noticed Abe and Ida. Bernard, one of Ida's bridge group, was glancing at them. Jean Green, Ida's enemy, twisted in her chair, hissing disapproval. Ida saw and tried to tug her hand from Abe's grip; he would not let go.

Sarah, who also noticed the stares, became angry with her sister. She appealed to Ida. "What about Charlie? He must be turning over in his grave. And what about Ma? What would Ma say?"

"Oh." Ida tugged her hand from Abe's. He smiled at her.

Ruby walked to their table with the turkey dinners.

Abe put his and Helen's into plastic containers. "I've got to get back to her." He glanced at Sarah and patted Ida's arm. They looked at each other. "I'll see you later," he told her. "We'll be fine." He wheeled away.

Sarah looked thoughtful. "I know what it is with him."

Ida was surprised. "What? Abe?"

"He's a doer. He doesn't think whether something is right or wrong."

"He wouldn't do anything wrong, Sarah."

"No. But he doesn't worry about that. He just goes after what he wants."

Ida sighed. "He says there isn't much time, Sarah."

Sarah shook her head, her eyes shut. "It doesn't take a genius to figure that out."

"He frightens me," Ida admitted.

"That's not going to stop him," Sarah predicted. "Except that Helen is there."

"He should put her on the third floor," Ida blurted.

"Ida!"

Ida was embarrassed. "I didn't mean it that way. I know he won't. It's just that it's so hard for him. That's all."

Sarah said, "What did he mean I'll see you later? Are you going to see him later? Where?"

Ida blushed and mouthed, "I don't know."

In bed, breathing oxygen, she was tense. *Is he coming here? What does he think is going to happen? I can't stand this. Oh, my God!*

Someone was tapping on her door. Ida felt her heart thump. More tapping. She did not move. The handle turned and the door opened. *Oh, God, I didn't lock it.*

"Ida . . . ?" Abe wheeled into the apartment. "Ida . . ." He rolled his chair into her bedroom.

"Abe," she murmured.

He wheeled close to her bed, bending to clear a clutter of magazines, books and tissues on the floor. "You should keep your room neater."

"I know, I'm sorry." *I used to keep things neat, Abe.*

"It doesn't matter. I can't stay long. I think she's going."

"Abe?" *I have to know.*

"What?"

"Abe?"

"What is it?"

"Why are you here?"

"I want us to be together."

"Abe, your wife is dying."

"I'm going to her. But I can be with you too."

"Maybe it's not right."

He looked angry. "To hell with that, Ida. She's been gone from me for a long time." He was urgent. "And we can be with each other now."

"Abe, I'm not sure I want this."

"You're frightened," he said in a soft voice. "I know you, Ida."

"No."

"Like a girl. You're like a girl."

Ida laughed. *Why did I laugh?* "Some girl." She laughed again. *This must be funny.* "I'm no girl, and you're no boy, mister. You're a crazy old man. Go back to your wife."

"See," he said. "We're good together."

She laughed again. "Go back to your apartment."

"I'm going." He took her hand, kissed it and wheeled to the door. "You'll see," he called to her.

Ida lay back on her pillow, staring at the ceiling. *Charlie, do you know what? Abe is courting me. And I love it.*

Helen died in the night. Ida saw the flashing red lights outside.

A few residents, courtesy of the Seven Oaks van, turned out for the service in the chapel of Kaufman's funeral parlor. Afterward, as they waited outside for the hearse and limousine, Ida stood close to Abe and pressed his arm. He did not seem to know she was there.

Ida and Sarah rode with Abe to Machpelah cemetery. After brief prayers, the rabbi spoke. "A kind and gentle woman. A good wife and companion, beloved by her husband and her friends. But now the Lord has gathered Helen to his bosom." He paused and said quietly, "Mr. Hirsch has asked me to announce that he would not be sitting shiva and that any charitable contributions should be made to our local Alzheimer's disease chapter." The rabbi recited the yahrzeit prayer for the dead, and the casket was lowered into the grave. Abe wheeled to the edge and reached for a shovel. He dropped a few clods onto the casket. He stayed there for a few moments, head down, eyes closed. He pulled himself back and wheeled down the gravel path to the limousine, his face a mask. Ida and Sarah followed slowly, dabbing their eyes.

For a few days, Abe was remote, eating with the sisters, not saying much. One evening, he knocked on Ida's door. Again, it was unlocked. She was in bed in her nightgown, over which she wore a pink nylon jacket embroidered with white lace around the collar and cuffs, for the third night in a row in case he came.

Abe wheeled to her side and sat quietly. He sighed and nodded, just being there, not speaking. Ida realized that she had never seen him when his face was not animated.

After a few minutes, she needed to speak or to hear him. She said, "So?"

He smiled briefly. "These days the sound of my own voice is more than I want to hear."

"You miss her."

"Of course. Forty-nine years."

"We were forty-four years when Charlie died."

"What did he die from?"

"They said that his heart just stopped. All of a sudden."

"That's how I want to go."

"Me too."

"Did you sit shiva, Ida?"

"For a few days. People came. I don't remember much. They gave me Valium and sleeping pills."

The bleak look on Abe's face frightened her. He said, "A long time ago, we sat shiva when my sister died. I hated it. That one time was enough for me."

They were quiet. Ida said, "What happened to your sister?"

Abe shook his head. "We were so close. She was so pretty. I begged her to be careful with that guy."

"She was pregnant?"

He nodded. "She had an abortion. They went to a butcher. Not a real butcher. I could have done better. A butcher doctor."

"And she died?"

"She died. It was the end of my family. Almost the end of everything. I went crazy for a long time." He shuddered.

"You have to grieve," she suggested.

"I grieved for Estelle," Abe said. "That Helen is gone is a blessing. I miss her. But I'm glad she is gone . . . I'm going back to my apartment now."

Ida took his hand and kissed it. "Good night, Abe."

"Good night, Ida."

He looked at her intently, inquiring.

She didn't understand what he wanted. "What is it, Abe?"

"I can come back?"

He had never seemed vulnerable before. She was surprised. "If you want."

Abe touched her hand, turned and wheeled out of the apartment.

Ida closed her eyes and listened to Jay Leno without looking at the TV picture. She felt cold and pulled the electric blanket to her chin. *Charlie? Are you mad at me, Charlie? Abe and I are different people. You and I were different too. But I understood you. Charlie, I feel lucky.*

At lunch, Abe shifted the ground from beneath them. He was talking about Seven Oaks. "Do people ever leave this place?"

Ida said, "You mean like for a trip or to visit someone?"

Abe shook his head. "I mean, like moving out."

Sarah laughed at him. "People come here because it's easier."

"The thing is," Abe said. "I'm making plans."

The sisters stared at him.

"You certainly don't waste time," Sarah murmured.

"I don't have time," he said. "We don't have time."

He edged his wheelchair toward Ida, reached out and stroked her cheek. She raised her hand and held Abe's fingers against her face. It was an involuntary gesture that she was barely aware of. He kissed her hand.

Sarah was unhappy. *What was that? What's going on? What are you two doing?*

Ida looked at Abe in surprise. "What happened?"

He smiled at her. "I've got a ball game to watch." He pushed back from the table and wheeled to the dining room door.

Sarah said, "Okay, what do you think you're doing with him?"

"I'm not sure, but I like it." She lifted her cup. Her hand shook, and she set it rattling back in the saucer.

Sarah said, "I think that he's using you."

"What do you mean?" Ida felt herself flushing. "How is he using me?"

"He just buried his wife, Ida. Don't tell me you think he's fallen in love with you. Please."

"I don't think anything, Sarah."

"He's a lonely man," Sarah said. "He wants the first woman that comes along."

"What a mean thing to say," Ida groaned. "You should be ashamed. Anyway, maybe I'm a lonely woman, and we're good for each other. What's wrong with that?" And she added, "It's not as if we're having some kind of romance, Sarah. Really."

Sarah hesitated. "Maybe I'm jealous. It wouldn't be the first time."

Ida carefully picked up her cup, anchoring her elbow on the table. She managed a sip of coffee, but when she tried to set the cup down, she spilled what was left in it. "Nuts."

They mopped with their napkins. Sarah said, "You're getting worse than Ma."

"Don't start, Sarah."

"All right. I won't start. But Abe's not going to put up with your pills."

"I just take what I need."

"He's not Charlie," Sarah said. "Charlie used to get pills for you. Abe won't put up with it."

Ida stood and headed for the entrance.

Sarah followed. She put her hand on Ida's arm. "Too bad. I wish I had your chance. You're going to ruin it."

"Maybe." Ida had tears in her eyes. "I'm trying, darn it."

That night in bed, waiting for Abe, Ida consulted Charlie. *Charlie, Sarah thinks that I'm making a fool of myself. I hope not. I don't want that to happen. I don't want to be embarrassed. But I think, who cares? What do I have to lose? Am I right? Oh, God, Charlie, please, I hope I'm right.*

She sighed and cried a little.

When Abe came and saw her teary eyes, he said, "You're more emotional than Helen. She didn't cry much."

"I know you loved her." Ida clapped her hand to her mouth, as if the words had popped out of their own volition. This was not a topic she wanted him to get started on.

Abe saw nothing wrong with it. "You and I talk," he explained. "It's natural and easy."

"Yes."

"Helen and I talked . . . the same way."

"Oh." She felt a twinge of disappointment.

"But she was a simpler person. You're smarter. And I'm still trying to figure you out. Anyway, I don't think in terms of love."

She was pleased that he considered her a mystery and was conscious of her heart beating. "What do you think in terms of?"

"Closeness. Sharing."

"That's nice."

"The opposite of loneliness."

"Yes." It was what Sarah had suggested.

He took her hand. "Ida, I want to hold you."

"What?"

"I want to get into your bed and hold you."

"Oh, Abe. I can't. It's been too long."

"What does that mean?" He sounded angry.

She was miserable. "I can't do that, Abe. You don't understand."

She felt dreamy. She wanted to talk to Charlie. Abe wouldn't let her. He grabbed her hand. "In my shop we got to know our customers. We knew which ones wanted it."

She shuddered. "What are you talking about?"

He wouldn't let go. "The young guys went after it. Is this too crude for you?"

She was angry. "I'm not one of those women."

"No, I know. And I'm not a young guy."

"What?"

"I'm an old guy. And I just want to hold you."

"My God." She felt confused.

"Okay?"

"My God," she whispered.

"You said that already," he pointed out.

She wanted desperately to consult Charlie. Abe wouldn't allow her to drift away. She gave up. "Okay, but don't squeeze. I have a lot of sore spots."

"That's my girl." He placed his hands on the bed and shifted himself out of the wheelchair.

"And no funny stuff."

"Of course not." He reached his arms around her slowly, carefully.

"This is crazy," she said.

"No, it isn't." He buried his face in her hair.

They both laughed from relief and pleasure.

They slept. At 3:00 a.m., Abe kissed her cheek and wheeled out of her room.

At last, she spoke with Charlie. *Did you see Abe hug me? In my bed? And I liked it. That's right. I liked it. I hope you didn't mind, Charlie. If you did, next time don't watch.*

8. The Four Musketeers

Miriam took Helen's place at their table. "All they do is complain at my table," she told Ida. "And talk about their symptoms. You people are livelier."

Ida liked the fact that Miriam considered her part of a lively table. Miriam was lively, no doubt about that. And she never really complained. Even if she described an annoying symptom, an aching joint, an underperforming body part—her heart sometimes lagged behind her legs, leaving her breathless, her memory was not perfect but whose was?—Miriam never sounded sorry for herself; it was almost as if she were outside of her body ("There goes that darn heart again," and sitting and laughing).

She isn't looking for sympathy, Ida realized. Abe doesn't want sympathy, she thought. Sarah doesn't either. Actually, Ida told herself, I don't either. We all keep going, she concluded. No matter what. She considered her pill-taking her way of keeping going. At the same time, she renewed her vow to keep it under control. No more falling down, she promised herself.

There was laughter at the table now. Miriam told funny stories about her son-in-law, a lawyer who made extra money as a process server (people hated him because he enjoyed the expression on their faces when he served them) and her daughter-in-law who was a host on a public television talk program. "A gay man got into a fight with a skinhead," she told them. "They had to call the police. Grace, my daughter-in-law, was in seventh heaven."

"Thelma Lewis's grandson is gay," Ida told them.

"A perfectly nice young man," Sarah said.

"I guess I don't understand it," Miriam said. "But live and let live is my motto. What do you think, Abe?"

"One of the guys that worked for me was queer," Abe said. "The other guys made him miserable, and he finally left."

Ida was not comfortable with Abe's use of *queer* and, thinking about what Larry King would say, decided to jump in on the side of social justice. "That's not right. What did you do about it?"

Abe smiled at her. "Nothing. What should I do? Have a meeting of my employees? Talk about alternative lifestyles?"

Ida smiled back at him. She loved the moment of intimacy.

"Actually," Abe said, "he was a good butcher, very fast with his knives. But the way he talked got on the other guys' nerves."

"What do you mean?" Miriam said.

"You know," Abe said. "He sounded . . . that way."

"Different," Ida said, still on her liberal tack.

"Sure," Abe agreed, not troubling himself about what he considered Ida's softheaded left-wing views. His relief over not having to worry about Helen was still taking hold. He felt easier than he had in years. And he liked to tell them stories about his long career in the butcher business. "This customer told one of my guys that he had a heavy thumb. 'Don't worry, lady,' the guy said to her, 'I'm including my thumb with your ground beef.'"

"I was the customer," Sarah said. They all stared at her and laughed, it was a joke from an unexpected source.

"How was the thumb?" Miriam said.

"Delicious," Sarah said.

Ida was happy. From time to time, when they were laughing loudly, she glanced around to see if other people in the dining room were looking at them.

In fact, Doris and Jean noticed. "What are you all laughing about?" Doris said to Ida as they accompanied her down the corridor after dinner.

"What's so funny?" Jean said.

"I didn't realize we were laughing," Ida lied.

"Your friend has gotten over his wife's dying," Doris said.

"Yes," Ida said. "It was a terrible burden."

Jean said, "Maybe he'll make a play for Miriam."

Ida's stomach lurched. "I don't think she's his type."

"You never know about men like that," Doris said.

"I hear he was a butcher," Doris said.

Ida nodded. "Abe owned a big butcher shop."

Doris said, "He's missing a leg."

Jean said, "So what? He's still a man."

"That's true," Doris tittered. "And what does a missing leg matter at our stage of the game?"

Ida was relieved to reach her room. She left them standing in the corridor without saying good night.

They're jealous, Charlie. Ida was in her bed. *Abe wouldn't be interested in either of them and they know it. Miriam is too old for him. He likes me.* Ida's hand moved to her vagina. *You don't have to look, Charlie.*

At dinner the next night, Miriam was quiet. Ida asked if something was the matter. Miriam told her that it was the anniversary of her husband's death. Abe asked her how long ago her husband had died. "Twenty years," Miriam replied. "But it seems like yesterday."

Abe looked pained. He shook his head.

Ida said, "Darn it."

Sarah twisted and untwisted her napkin. She said quietly, "It feels like three dead people are sitting with us . . . You're all lucky."

Ida patted Sarah's hand.

Miriam said to Abe, "What was your wife like?"

He let out a long breath. "You mean before her mind went?"

"Yes."

"She was gentle," he said. "But she could be tough, if she had to."

"Were you close?" It was a "Miriam" question, direct, to the essence of the matter.

Abe smiled. "We were close."

"I thought so," Miriam said.

"It was best when we were with each other, just us."

Miriam understood. "Yes."

"Like two old shoes." Abe laughed.

Ida pretended to sneeze and wiped her eyes with her napkin. "No, Abe," she said.

"What's the matter with old shoes?" he said.

Ruby was there, waiting to take their orders. "If you are planning on eating dinner tonight," she told them.

"She's changed," Abe said to Ida after Ruby departed.

Sarah said, "She knows we're not just old crocks."

Ida touched Sarah's hand again. "You've always been so smart." She said to Miriam, "My sister has always known what's going on."

Sarah shrugged. "I had to."

Miriam said, "So did my Harold. He had to. He was a psychoanalyst."

They stared at her. None of them had ever known a psychoanalyst. Abe said, "You mean like with people on the couch?"

Miriam nodded.

Sarah said, "What did he actually do?"

"It's hard to explain," Miriam said. "He helped people with their personal problems."

Ida said, "For years."

Miriam agreed. "Usually for years."

Abe said, "What kind of husband was he?"

"He was very busy," Miriam said. "He loved his work. We both had our own lives."

"Apart from each other?" Abe was sympathetic.

"I didn't mean that," Miriam said. "I meant that we were independent, and we were close. But we each went our own way a lot."

Ruby quietly set down bowls of soup, tiptoeing around the table. They were hardly aware of her, thinking about what Miriam had said, thinking about their own lives. They dipped spoons into their bowls, lifting and swallowing soup as if each spoonful contained wisdom and understanding. After a while, Miriam said to Ida, "What about your husband?"

Sarah looked quickly at Ida and concentrated on her soup.

Ida nodded. "We were close. Charlie made me happy."

Abe murmured, "He was good to you?"

"Yes."

"Were you good to him?" Miriam said.

"I tried to be," Ida said. She added, "It wasn't always easy. Sarah knows."

They were quiet again. Miriam said, "Well, I haven't had a conversation like this in a long time."

"I've never had a conversation like this," Abe said.

Ida nodded. "Neither have I." She sighed and felt an impulse to add to her description of her marriage, to let the others know more. "Our last years were bad," she said quietly.

They watched her.

"We were distant. I took too many pills. He moved to the other bedroom."

"It happens." Abe was sympathetic.

Ida laughed a little. "I don't know why I wanted you to know all that."

Miriam said, "It was group therapy. We should do it again."

Sarah agreed. "The four musketeers. We should do it again."

Miriam said to Ida, "Are you going to play bingo tonight?"

Ida said, "No, I'm playing bridge. And you'll be into the Internet," she said to Abe.

"The Tigers are talking about trading their best player," he told her.

"What's the matter with them," said Miriam who knew nothing about baseball. "Don't they want to win?"

"Good question," Abe said. "And I'll straighten them out."

9. The Bumpy Road to Love

It was a holiday that most of the residents had lost track of. Martin Luther King's Birthday? Columbus Day? Washington's Birthday?

In the dining room, daisies in white vases were set on the tables next to peach-colored napkins that were folded into little towers. The flowers were provided by the Friends of Seven Oaks whose mission was to raise the morale of their mothers, fathers, aunts, uncles, cousins and longtime friends. A few smiling FSO members had arrived a half hour before lunch to fold the napkins and lingered to report on the reactions of the diners who were covertly prodded by the staff to utter cries of surprise and appreciation.

Ida passed between tables occupied by people still murmuring about the daisies, but now were becoming attentive to platters of seeded and plain rolls and pats of butter and margarine, to wicker baskets filled with crisp celery, carrots, olives, tasty cherry tomatoes and to small glass bowls of fruit salad waiting next to their dinner plates.

With her hair rinsed blond, her lips an orange red, her nails painted bright red, her cheeks rouged and wearing a red-and-orange ceramic pin that she had made herself in arts and crafts, Ida took pride in her appearance in this world of what she had called "last-time-around survivors." And there was the reassuring contrast with her sister, Sarah, who was waiting at their table. *We've always been so different. How could two sisters be so different?*

Sarah's face was more lined than her older sister's. Her white hair was twisted into a coil and pinned to the back of her head. Having taught herself to accept disappointment and loneliness, Sarah did not trust daydreams and told her friends that she did not believe that with luck anything was possible.

Ida puffed and lowered herself into her chair. "Where is Abe?" She cleared her throat.

"Oh," Sarah said. "Your boyfriend. Maybe he's found another woman.

There are plenty of them here to choose from."

Ida did not bother to respond. She was looking for Abe in his wheelchair. "I don't know where he is."

"He's late." Sarah was irritated. "It's his own affair. Let me have the rolls, please."

"There must be a reason. He's always here. He always eats."

"Ida. Look at me."

"What?"

"You sound like a teenager. Stop it."

"Oh." Ida slumped in her chair.

Halfway through lunch and still no Abe, Ida put down her napkin and stood. "I need to see if he's okay."

Sarah went with her.

"You don't have to come," Ida said.

"I know. You don't have to tell me."

Ida knocked on Abe's door. There was no response. "Abe," she called out. "It's me."

Sarah pointed out that they didn't know if he was in there.

Ida shuddered. "Something's wrong."

"What could be wrong?"

"Sarah, please. Get someone."

"Phooey," Sarah said and hurried down the corridor.

When Mrs. Smithers opened Abe's door, they found him in bed, barely breathing, white as his sheet.

Ida collapsed into a chair. Mrs. Smithers called 911 and the Seven Oaks nurse. Sarah said to Ida, "How did you know that something was wrong?"

"Diabetic coma," the nurse said as they wheeled Abe away.

Ida wept. Sarah said, "Come on. We'll go to your room."

"Abe," Ida groaned as they walked down the corridor.

Sarah told her that Abe would be fine. "They'll fix him up and send him back."

"How do you know?"

"Remember Fannie Katzman. Same thing. They gave her an intravenous and discharged her."

"She's dead now."

"But she was fine then."

Sarah had an odd look on face. She touched Ida's arm. "I can't believe this has happened to you."

Ida stared at her sister and resumed walking. "I need my oxygen."

In bed, oxygen flowing, Sarah gone at last, the TV on, Ida had a glimmering of a headache and her hand went automatically to her pain pills, an action that she was not even aware of. She comforted herself with two Darvons and two Empirins and, for good measure, an Antivert in case she napped and felt dizzy when she awoke. She indulged her instinct for the awful: *What if Abe dies? And I never meet anyone like him again? Charlie, Sarah called him my boyfriend. Charlie, is it too late for me? I'm not eighty yet* .

When she woke, still fretting over Abe and to prolong her pleasant numb feeling, Ida swallowed two more Darvons and, for good measure, a Percocet.

At dinner, to her surprise, Abe wheeled through the dining room door, pale and moving cautiously. This was unsettling because she was used to seeing him spin down the long corridors like an aging Hell's Angel, his amputated leg sticking out like a figurehead of a land-based ship on wheels: for Ida, this image was a confirmation of what she considered her original creativity.

Abe was embarrassed at having to be carted away in an ambulance, so he shouted at them. "I was dumb. I fell asleep and forgot my injection. It's your fault. You distracted me," he told Ida who was worried now because she was having trouble focusing on what he was saying and knew that she would never be able to speak clearly because her lips and tongue felt thick. It seemed unfair. *Abe, I didn't expect you. And I was upset or I would never have taken all those pills.*

She decided to use as few words as she could, but still slurred, "You almost died." Her almost sounded like *almosht*. Her lower lip drooped. She tried to smile at him, but her smile was a grimace. *No use, no use.*

He was frowning. "I'm fine. These days they throw you out of the hospital. What's with you?"

Sarah intervened. "Ida knew that something was wrong, she made me get help." She glanced at Ida who was staring at her plate. Sarah continued, "Well, this is what happened, Abe. Ida says to me, 'Sarah, something is wrong. Abe never misses a meal, even with this food.'"

He agreed, "Even with this food, I've got an appetite."

"So I ran to get Mrs. Smithers," Sarah concluded.

Ida knew that she was sitting stiffly. She did a kind of shimmy, trying to relax. "Don't feel good," she hissed.

Abe stared at her. Ida giggled. Abe turned to Sarah. "I'm not hungry." He pushed his wheelchair from the table.

Ida did not speak or look up.

Sarah said, "Shouldn't you eat something?"

"I've got stuff in my apartment," he said and, after staring once more at Ida, wheeled out of the dining room.

Later, after Jay Leno, after two more Darvons and a Sominex, Ida was still awake and staring at the TV screen, which seemed blurred. When Abe knocked on her door, she did not respond. He called, "Ida, . . . Ida, let me in. Listen to me. Have you taken more pills? Ida, we have to talk." She heard the creak of his wheelchair moving away. She wept. *Charlie, I'll tell him I was sleeping. He couldn't know that I wasn't asleep.*

At lunch the next day, Abe moved to a table on the other side of the dining room. Sarah was outraged. "Why did he do that? You saved his life."

Ida decided that her best tactic was resignation. "Maybe it just wasn't meant to be."

Sarah was shrill. "No, Ida. You could have. But you had to take those pills. And you were doing so much better."

With her fork, Ida made tracks on her paper place mat. The tracks became a large X. "Sarah, it wasn't my fault," she explained. "Couldn't you tell? I was so upset."

Sarah mourned, "We both liked him. He was good for us."

The next day, Millie, the large blond hostess, told the sisters that she would have to assign a couple to their table. Ida was numb with dismay, but Sarah said, "Give it a few more days, Millie."

Along with the entire dining room crowd, Millie had noted Abe's move. She hooted, "You got it, ladies."

Ida said, "Sarah, he's not coming back."

"Probably not," Sarah agreed. "But we can leave the space open for a while."

A few days later, Ida and Sarah attended a slide show in the card room. "A special treat," Mrs. Smithers had announced. "Don't miss it."

The sisters were in the front row. Lights began to blink on the screen. Trumpets blared, drums rolled. The title of the show flashed: "South Beach!" Then they heard, "Hottest of the Hot! Your day in the Sun!" The theme from Miami Vice played. The residents applauded. It was a tour, via slides and an audiotape complete with music, of South Beach, Miami Beach's "glamorous, revitalized art deco miracle, the Southland's trendy enclave for celebrities. Look, there's Sylvester Stallone, there's Jay Leno. Oh, oh, there's Madonna!

"And look at this, folks. Hotels in blue, pink and tan, with neon lights ala the 1930s. The Raleigh, the lavish Delano, the economical Park Central, the Beacon, the Governor, and the ultimate, the Ritz-Carlton. And don't forget the beach. Glorious, warm sand, heavenly water. Just kick back and soak up the sun, with or without your bathing suit (the residents tittered) . . . but don't forget your sunscreen. And don't miss the grand new boardwalk for folks who want to take in the scene on the beach.

"South Beach. Gorgeous South Beach. Make your plans now for an unforgettable vacation."

Dark room. Flashing lights. Music to a smashing climax. Lights on to enthusiastic applause.

"Fat chance," Ida said as they filed to the exit.

"I wouldn't mind," Sarah replied, "if somebody wanted to treat me."

"Thank you, Mr. Hirsch," Mrs. Smithers called out.

"You're welcome," Abe said from a corner of the room.

The sisters froze. A hint of a smile on his face, Abe rolled his wheelchair to them.

Sarah said, "That was your show?"

He was casual. "I arranged for it."

Unreasonably, Ida felt dizzy with hope. "Why, Abe?"

"I want to go there."

"Really?" Sarah said.

He said that he been looking at South Beach on the Internet and saw this slide show advertised. "I wanted to see it." He hesitated. "I bought plane tickets. And I made a reservation at the Delano Hotel."

Ida guessed what was coming. "Really, Abe?"

He looked at her, challenging. "For two people, Ida."

"Abe." She felt uncertain. "That's great."

Great because Abe still wanted to be with her. Great. Even though Sarah said, "Can't three go for almost what it would cost for two?"

Ida grabbed her sister's sleeve. Sarah looked at her. "What's the matter?"

"Guess what?" Ida said.

Sarah laughed. She knew what this was about.

Ida hid her face in her hands. She whispered, "I can't believe it. I'm not sure I can make it in the outside world. That's so dumb."

Sarah patted Ida's head. "You're not the only one."

Ida smiled at Abe through tears. He looked somber.

After dinner, he was in Ida's room in his wheelchair next to her bed, talking over the hum of the oxygen pump. She wore a nylon bed jacket over her nightgown. He took her hand. She smiled, expecting him to get into bed. But he stayed in his chair. "Ida, we need to talk about your pills."

Ida shuddered. She realized that she hadn't understood how upset he was. "No, dear. We don't need to."

"The pills are bad for you." He sounded harsher than he had intended.

Wrong, Abe. You're wrong. She sat back, her black eyes darting. "Abe, I just take what I need."

He made an effort to be calm, not to challenge or frighten her. "No, Ida. You know that's not true. Sometimes you can't talk straight. It's not good to hear you or see you."

She responded in a cold voice. "Why are you saying this to me?"

"I have to. It's the only way."

"You're making me cry."

"I don't care if you cry. If you want to come to South Beach, you have to cut way down on your pills."

She was appalled. "My doctor prescribes my pills. Otherwise I suffer."

"You take the pills for more than pain. It's one pill for pain and another pill for Ida."

She flared at him. "You may as well go without your wheelchair."

"What? That's dumb. You know it. For God's sakes, Ida, what are you doing?"

She had begun to rock, bending her head forward almost to her knees, sitting up abruptly, down, up, down, up.

"Ida, what's wrong? What's wrong with you?"

She heard him dimly and rocked like she used to when she was a child. His words grated. Her hand reached for her pill drawer.

He yelled, "Ida, no!"

She took out three bottles of pills, turned away from him, flipped open the tops, poured pills into one hand and tossed them into her mouth.

"No, damn it." Abe jumped onto her bed and clapped her back. "No, Ida. No, dear. Open your mouth."

She was grinding the pills.

He forced her head forward and shook her. "No, Ida. No, sweetheart. Spit it out! Do it! Now! Spit it! Spit it!"

She did, into his hand, a mixture of saliva and pill fragments that he clenched in his fist. He got back into his wheelchair. She lay on her pillow, eyes closed.

Abe leaned over in his wheelchair, his head near hers. "That was not funny, Ida."

What? Funny? What is Abe saying?

He spoke softly into her ear. "I know you're not understanding me."

She opened one eye and the other, surprising him. "Go away."

"No."

"Go away."

"I'm not done."

"What?"

"I'm going to wait right here until you can listen to me."

She closed her eyes again. He wheeled to the bathroom to clean his hand.

Half an hour later, they looked at each other. Abe said, "Okay?"

Ida pouted, said nothing.

He was angry. "You're going to have to decide. I'm going to South Beach. If you want to come, you'll have to bring only a few pills, just enough to get by. No extras. You decide."

Abe touched her hand, turned and wheeled out of the apartment. Ida put on the TV earphones.

Jay Leno was talking with a blonde whose skirt ended at her crotch. She kept tugging at her hem, crossing and recrossing her legs. Leno said, "Let us know when you find a comfortable position." The audience laughed.

The girl laughed, embarrassed. "My agent wanted me to wear this silly thing," she confessed.

"Would you like a shawl or something?" Leno asked.

The girl nodded. "Bring her something," Leno said to someone off camera. "We have a modesty problem here." A man handed the girl a pretty brown-and-red paisley shawl. She covered her legs. The audience applauded. "So," Leno said, "what else does your agent get you to do?" The audience laughed.

"Oh, no," the girl said. "Jimmy's a nice guy."

Leno nodded and said, "He's doing his job. It's part of show business."

"That's what Jimmy says," the girl agreed. Leno made a face. The audience laughed again. Ida took off the earphones and closed her eyes. She reached for her pill bottles.

Ida?

She held the bottles.

Who said that? Was it Leno? She picked up the earphones. No. Jay was laughing with some young male movie star whose name she could not possibly remember, though she knew that she had seen him before. *Was it on Oprah's show?*

Ida?

What? Who said that?

It's me, Larry.

Larry? King? Oh, God.

It's time to be strong, Ida.

Why? Why do I have to be strong? I don't want to be strong. I don't happen to be a strong person.

Ida, that's not true. You're a strong person. You're one of the strongest people I know.

What do you want from me, Larry?

Look at what you're doing, Ida . . . the pills . . . Look at what's happening here.

What? What's happening? Why do I have to know what's happening?

If you don't want to see, I can't help you, Ida.

Larry, you know what? I'm in my bed. I'm going to take my pills. That's the end of it.

I'm disappointed, Ida.

Listen to me, Larry.

Yes?

Who knows if I'm even going with him to South Beach? I'm used to it here, Larry.

And your pills are here, right?

Good night, Larry.
Good night, Ida.

She turned off the TV. She thought about the bottles in her hand. She began to sweat. Her nightgown was soaked. She breathed deeply, rapidly. Her heart pounded. She was ashen when she reached for the phone to call her sister.

Sarah prided herself on being a woman who was cool in emergencies. She grabbed Ida's hand and said, "Have you fainted? What's the matter? Talk to me."

When Ida groaned, Sarah said, "Come on, snap out of it."

Ida was shocked into alertness. "Sarah?"

"What?"

"Abe wants me to cut down on my pills in South Beach."

Sarah's words cut like little knives. "Ida dear, I don't think you can do that. You're dependent . . . you know it. It's too late for you to really cut down, isn't that right? I'm afraid that you're going to make yourself sick. Really sick."

The sisters looked at each other.

"I know," Ida said. "But what else can I do? I have to try. Anyway, I did it for a while, didn't I?"

After a long silence, Sarah, her voice suddenly wheedling, said, "Ida, in South Beach, do you expect that you and Abe are going to . . . ?"

Ida, at last, had something to smile about. "I'll write you a postcard, Sarah."

"I can't stand this," Sarah left her, walking stiffly.

For Ida, this conversation led to an unwanted and unexpected aftermath, a cold feeling of anxiety, a dart of concern and a memory of herself and Charlie on their honeymoon when lovemaking led to pain and a lack of pleasure. Her romance novels had hinted strongly at something that was missing. And in their long marriage, sex never became really good, okay at best, but never great; never a union with passionate closeness, rather a quick impersonal act that ended in rapid withdrawal and a feeling of loneliness. She did not mind when their sex life ended. It happened to lots of long-married couples, didn't it?

Ida suspected strongly that Abe was looking forward to sex, and she did not really know if she wanted it. She was worried about a replication of past misery. This was a secret worry that she buried beneath another worry about actually leaving Seven Oaks.

She somehow got through the night by taking just three Tylenols.

The next day she decided that she had to make Abe understand that she was concerned about going away with him. "I feel safe here," she told him. "Everything is taken care of."

She did not realize that Seven Oaks had only provided Abe what he needed to take care of Helen. With her gone, he hated living in a place that was so organized and predictable, where, in his view, seniors who used to lead independent lives waited helplessly for inevitable physical and mental decay.

"To hell with that," Abe said. And mystifying her, he added, "I'm not done with living." He didn't tell her that he was already making plans to leave Seven Oaks, for the two of them to live on their own.

He kissed her hand. "Ida, you're worried about your pills. Sarah probably doesn't think you can stop. But in South Beach, you'll do it. We're going to be happy there. Trust me. I know you better than you know yourself."

She sighed and shook her head. *Easy to say, mister. What if I can't?*

He read her mind. "I have an important question."

"What?"

"Do you still own a bathing suit?"

She laughed.

"You're going to need one."

"I can't wear a bathing suit anymore. I would look terrible."

"What are you talking about? I'm going to wear one. How do you think I'm going to look?"

10. South Beach

The Delano Hotel was narrow and white outside and in. White columns in the lobby reached to a high white ceiling. There was a white cocktail bar with high, white-cushioned barstools. Long, filmy white curtains stretching from floor to ceiling and wall to wall divided the lobby from a second room and then a third. Wide white upholstered chairs and couches were placed along the walls.

The third room led to a flagstone terrace and down several flights of marble steps to a narrow pool. It was a long way to the pool and to a small sand beach beyond. Abe and Ida managed because of an elevator installed for wheelchair access, which was why Abe had chosen the Delano; that, and he liked the whiteness he saw in the hotel brochure.

Ida gasped when the bellman led them into their ocean-facing room and was silent when he pulled the curtains and opened the glass sliding door to their terrace, letting them pause to take in the sight and sound of the breakers. He showed them the minibar and the large tiled bathroom with its huge tub and bidet. Later she explained to Abe about the bidet, she had traveled in Europe.

Exhausted by the trip, Ida sunk onto the bed. "This is as big as my whole bedroom," she said. "Well, maybe not that big . . . and I'm not asking how much this costs a night."

Abe told her that the money didn't matter, that this was their special time.

He lifted himself onto the bed and embraced her. Ida's head was on his shoulder, his arm around her. With the Florida light filtered by the curtains and the outside noises, laughter, shouts, dimly heard, they slept.

An hour later, Abe woke her by kissing her cheek.

She said, "I'm dreaming. Kiss me here." She touched a place on her neck. He kissed that spot and other spots and surprised her by sitting up.

"We're going for a walk now," he said. "We'll come back to the hotel and have dinner."

In bathing suits and robes, both of them were aware of curious glances from the younger folk and so a little defiant and pleased with themselves, they moved slowly down the boardwalk, her hand on his wheelchair, and stared at the tanned bodies. "Abe," Ida said. "Those girls are topless."

"Where?" He hoisted himself in his wheelchair.

"Abe . . ." She pushed him back into the chair. "You're going to hurt yourself."

"Nuts," he said, rising again. "Why do you think I came to South Beach?"

They returned to the hotel. Sleek young people chattering, laughing, populated the pool. But old-time music broadcast by hidden loudspeakers cheered Abe and Ida.

> Pack up all my cares and woe
> Here I go, feeling low,
> Bye, bye blackbird.

They smiled at the song and looked at the boys and girls in bathing suits that made cheerfully fraudulent claims of modesty. Abe gazed at a busty girl, the pieces of her bathing suit covering her nipples and crotch, nothing else.

Ida said, "Fifty years ago, that was me." She glanced at herself. "But not in that bathing suit."

"I used to look like that kid." Abe pointed to a blond muscled god whose low-slung bathing suit promoted his genitals.

"You have less hair now," she said in a gentle voice. "Especially on your head, pardon me."

He laughed. "The trick is to focus on what you've got."

"Unfortunately I have a lot more of everything."

Abe was reflective. "I used to be a fast runner."

She touched his hand. "Now you're a fast talker."

"Helen taught me."

She looked away. "Abe, your wife is still with you."

He seemed sad. "Well, I guess our mates want to hang around."

She was smug. "You don't have to worry about Charlie. I didn't tell him we were coming here."

He laughed. "Good. Anyway, I'm hungry. Let's have dinner."

Later, in their room, Ida sat on the bed; she was frightened. *I'm supposed to undress. I don't know what to do. I need my pills. Please, Abe, you can't imagine how much I need my pills. What if I took one or two, he wouldn't have to know. Right? No, he would see.*

Abe wheeled around the room, turning off lights and pleased by a familiar stirring in his genitals. He knew he had to go slowly. There was so much for them both to get used to, their unfamiliar bodies, him with his missing leg. How would Ida react to that? She hadn't minded when they lay together at Seven Oaks, she in her nightgown, he fully dressed. Abe took off his clothes except for his underpants and climbed onto the big bed next to her. He heard her nervous gasps.

"We're just going to look out the terrace door," he soothed. "I'll show you some stars. Then we'll sleep."

She felt like when she was a little girl. "Okay." Her voice was squeaky.

Sitting on the end of their king-sized bed, with Abe's arm around her waist, they looked at palm trees waving against the night sky, interrupting then allowing glimpses of the crescent moon that was upside down as if, he told her, it was waiting for a load of stars and possibly a planet or two. He pointed to Venus and her less bright partner, Jupiter. "Stars twinkle, planets do not," he told her. "Don't you want to put on your nightgown?"

"Don't look." She began to unbutton her dress.

He took a chance. "Ida, I'm proud of you."

She knew what he meant. *Abe won't let me take my pills.* She wanted to weep. *He won't let me.*

In their bed under the covering sheet, she sighed, his arm around her, protecting her against herself.

He reached for her hand. He courted and comforted her with loving words, distracting her to the point that she wished he would stop talking and do something. But when he touched her breast, fear was triggered, and she pushed his hand away.

Abe was oblivious. He had so much dammed up in him. He wanted to talk about sex and make love to her at the same time. He said, "Sweetheart, love is when you are close to somebody and trust them and share everything. Sex is part of that, a big part of that. It's part of the sharing that you can't do without. Or else there is an empty place in you, a part of you dies."

She felt herself sliding into a sexual state. *It's working.* She was exultant. *He's doing it.*

He stroked her thigh, but didn't stop talking. He was wooing her with words. "Loving somebody and having loving sex with them is the definition of happiness."

He put his hand on her breast again. This time she let him touch her nipple.

Her breathing quickened. "Oh, Abe. Oh, Abe."

She was swept away by his talk about love and by his gentle touching. He rolled on top of her. But to his dismay and her surprise, he was not firm enough to enter her, particularly since she was not moist.

For all her confusion, Ida certainly remembered what it was like to have an erect penis inside her. She realized that Abe was not that way. She embraced and consoled him. This she could do. "You're wonderful. I love you."

Abe, who was preoccupied by what he considered his failure, realized that she was sensitive to his problem. "Ida. I knew it. I knew it."

"Wait," she said and reached into the drawer of her nightstand for a tube of ointment she had placed there, next to her bottle of pills, which he hadn't asked about and she hadn't mentioned.

She held up the ointment. "My, God," he murmured.

They touched each other and felt and remembered and were close, wonderfully close. And somehow, with them pushing against each other, he managed to have an orgasm and after a moment, so did she, not a strong one, but compared with so many years of no sex with a man, it was a definite experience and a huge relief.

They slept fitfully in each other's arms, holding one another, holding on for dear life.

She awoke in the middle of the night thinking about her pills. Just a few. That's all. She slid open her drawer and grasped the bottle. He stirred. She had to move quickly. Because her movements were so surreptitious, so rapid, she had more pills in her hand than she intended and had no choice but to swallow them and hope that she would not be affected in the morning.

Bad luck.

It was still dark outside when they awoke. They kissed. She was afraid to speak, of slurring.

He put his nose into her neck and breathed in her scent. She was rigid. He said, "What's the matter? Are you upset?"

"No." Her voice sound strained.

He confronted her. "Are you okay?"

Time to face the music, kiddo. She had to speak. Slowly, carefully, she tried. "Abe, last night. I woke up and couldn't go back to sleep." (She said *shleep*.) She went on, "I took a few pills, only a few."

Had she slurred again? She wasn't sure. She couldn't tell from his face in the almost dark room.

He surprised her. "I want to go down to the boardwalk. I want to watch the sunrise from the boardwalk. I promised myself that I would do that."

She sat up and looked out the terrace door. The sky was lightening. "Okay." It was all she dared to say.

"Ida, please bring my wheelchair and my robe." Now she could hear that he was angry. He kept talking. "We've got to get going or we're going to miss it." He would not look at her.

"Okay." She moved rapidly, bringing his robe and wheelchair. She felt misunderstood and wanted to defend herself against his unspoken accusation. She said, "I tried, Abe. Do you think I haven't tried?"

This was better because her frustration had driven out the words clearly.

He put on his robe and hopped into the chair, still not looking at her.

She kept after him. "Do you have any idea how hard this has been for me?" She wasn't pleading anymore.

As they left the room for the elevator, he shook his head but did not speak. She wasn't done. "Listen, Abe, I've been trying. And if you're mad at me, that's too bad."

They emerged from the hotel and headed for the boardwalk. He sighed and softly cursed.

"Okay, Abe," she said. "Have it your way. But I'll tell you what. I want to go back to Seven Oaks. I want to be in my own bed in my own room. With my pills." There, I said it.

"You're a quitter," he said finally.

She stopped and actually spun around and clapped her hands. "I get it," she shouted. "I understand what this is all about."

He gaped. "What are you saying?"

She pointed her finger at him. "You thought that if we made love, I wouldn't need my pills."

He hesitated and said, "You're right."

"I almost thought so too," she admitted. "At least you're honest, Abe."

"Let's go faster," he said. "The sun is here."

Onto the boardwalk they went and watched the sun levitate above the horizon. Subdued, he said, "Sometimes I like to manage things."

She knew that this was as close to an apology that he could bring himself to make. She nodded. "That's right."

They looked at the brightening sky and wondered what the day would bring.

Questions
for Group Discussion

Part One: The Haberman Family

1. How do you think Devorah's issues affected the marriage of Yussel and Bertha?

2. How would you describe Ida? Which of the following apply to her personality: pretty, vain, spoiled, smart, socially ambitious, looking for love, insecure, generous, sympathetic, alert, interesting, imaginative, jealous, brave, self-starting, thoughtful.

3. Do you know anybody like her?

4. How would you describe Sarah? Which of the following apply: realistic, low self-esteem, accepting of her fate, content to play second-fiddle to Ida, lazy, jealous, smart, thoughtful, ambitious, lonely, supportive

5. Do you know anybody like her?

6. Do you relate more to Ida or Sarah?

7. Do you think Bertha or Yussel had a stronger influence on the development of Ida and Sarah?

8. What are your feelings about the value that women placed on being married in the earlier part of the century?

9. How do you think Sarah felt towards boys/men?

10. Describe your feelings towards unions in general and Sammy's involvement with the union? What does it say about the state of the country at that time?

11. How do you feel about Sarah's affair with Sammy? Do you think it affected her attitude towards men later in life?

12. What did you think of Josh?

13. Did you feel he was unfair to Sarah in leading her on when he knew he had had TB?

14. Were you surprised about Sergeant Boylan's approach to Ida?

15. How do you feel about his reaction after she rejected him?

16. How do you think Ida felt about Sergeant Boylan asking her out?

Part Two: The Hirsch Family

1. What do you think about the marriage of Reva and Morris?

2. How do you feel about how the parents' relationship impacted on Abe and Estelle?

3. What do you think about the sexual tension between Abe and Estelle? Is it appropriate? Do you think Abe had sexual feelings towards Estelle?

4. Was Abe a good brother to Estelle?

5. How do you think Abe felt about Estelle's sexual activities with other men?

6. Why do you think the other kids didn't like Estelle?

7. What feelings do you think Abe had towards his mother?

8. What was he feeling when he said goodbye to his mother for the last time?

9. Which of the following applies to Abe: brave, stubborn, controlling, insightful, energetic, independent, sympathetic, self-centered

10. Do you like Abe? Do you know anybody like him? What do you think of him as a person?

11. What do you think of Dan? How do you think he influenced Abe's development?

12. Do you think Dan was proud of Abe and Estelle?

13. Do you think Dan loved Reva?

14. How do you think Dan's death impacted on Abe and Estelle?

15. What do you think of Tillie's relationship with Abe?

16. Do you think Abe felt used by Tillie? Do you think he had real feelings for her? How do you think Estelle felt about Abe being with women?

17. Do you think Abe was confident about his looks and sexuality?

18. Do you know married couples who have casual extra-marital flings? How do you feel about being monogamous even if you are unhappy in a marriage or relationship?

19. Do you think Morris ever satisfied Reva?

20. How do you think Estelle and Abe felt about the possibility of Dan being their father?

21. The book mentions that people of different cultures actually look different. How do you feel about these stereotypes? How do you think these stereotypes affected Estelle's relationship with Tim Ryan?

22. How do you think Estelle's death effected Abe? Reva? Morris?

23. What are your views on abortion?

Part Three: The Nollman Family

1. How would you describe Charlie? Which of the following apply: fears women, loves women, loves Ida, honest, ambitious, emotionally independent

2. Do you know anybody like him? What do you think of that person?

3. Why was Charlie attracted to Ida?

4. How do you feel about the Nollman's entrepreneurial spirit to start a business?

5. How did you feel about Susie hanging out at Smith's Saloon? Do you think she was being sexual with any of the men in the bar?

6. How do you think growing up around so many women affected Charlie?

7. How do you feel about shadkins? Can you relate this concept to today's dating sites?

8. Do you think the sisters landed up in good relationships?

9. Do you think Naomi was controlling and manipulative?

10. How do you think Josiah and Max felt after having apologized to Naomi about taking her to King Lear to teach her a lesson?

11. Do you think Charlie was happy with his career choice?

12. What do you think the sexual life was like between Ida and Charlie?

13. How did you feel about Heather Sweetland? Do you think she was a user? How do you feel about people who use their looks to get what they want?

14. In life, relationships form in various ways. What did you think of the train interactions?

15. How did you feel about Pennington? Did you find him humorous? Generous? Kind? Happy?

16. How do you think Charlie felt about hanging around with someone who had so much money?

17. How did you feel about the sanitarium to lose weight? Do you think a place like this exists in today's society?

Part Four: Match Made In Heaven

1. Do you think it was exciting for Ida to be in Miami Beach?

2. Do you think Charlie was the man of her dreams?

3. Do you think Charlie misled Ida about his financial status?

4. How do you think Ida felt about Flo's relationship with Ken Ross?

5. Do you think it's surprising that Sarah actually had sex before Ida?

6. Do you think Ida liked sex?

7. Do you think receiving attention from men was important for Ida's self-worth and confidence?

8. Do you think the attention Ida received from men gave her superiority over Sarah?

9. Do you think Sarah was jealous over Ida's marriage?

10. Do you think Charlie was selfish to be concerned about sex during Ida's pregnancy?

11. How do you think the news about losing one of the twins's affected the marriage of Ida and Charlie?

12. Do you think Ida was a good mother?

13. Do you think Lena's affair with the lifeguard was appropriate?

14. Do you think Ida drove Charlie to have an affair with Martha?

15. Do you think he really felt bad about having an affair?

16. Do you think he had other affairs after Martha?

17. How do you think Ida really felt about the affair?

18. Do you think Ida should have questioned Charlie further?

19. How do you think the affair affected their relationship?

Part Five: Seven Oaks

1. What do you make of Ida's relationship with Larry King?
2. What do you think Ida gets out of it?
3. What do you think of Ida's son, Freddy?
4. Do you think Freddy was right in putting her at Seven Oaks?
5. Why do you think Sarah chose to go to Seven Oaks?
6. Why do you think Freddy hates visiting his mother at Seven Oaks?
7. If Fred hated these types of places, why do you think he put Ida in such a place?
8. Do you think Ida felt comfortable with the attention she received from Abe?
9. What do you think of Ida's pill addiction? Do you know people like her?
10. Do you think Ida can survive without her pills?
11. Do you think Ida misses Charlie?
12. What did you think about Jean's obsession with bread? Do you know people like her?
13. What are your feelings about assisted living facilities?
14. What do you think about the relationship between the staff at Seven Oaks and the residents? Do you know people in these types of facilities? Are they treated similarly?
15. How do you feel about the social groups that formed at Seven Oaks?
16. Do you think Charlie and Ida's relationship impacted on who Fred chose for his wife?
17. Why do you think Natalie left him?
18. How do you feel about the jealousy between Jean and Ida? How do you think it impacted on the sons?
19. Why do you think Sarah did not go out with Josh after seeing him at Seven Oaks?
20. Do you think they still had feelings for each other?
21. Do you think Ida wanted Sarah to go out with Josh?
22. Do you think Ida is dependent on Sarah?

Part Six: Ida and Abe

1. Do you think Abe brought Ida back to life?
2. How do you think Ida felt about Abe's wife, Helen? How long after a spouse passes away is an appropriate amount of time to wait before dating someone else?
3. Did you think it was right for Ida and Abe to be flirting while Helen was still alive? Do you think Helen knew?
4. Do you think its right for people to look for a new love interest if their spouse is in a state of dementia?

5. Why do you think Abe never used crutches?

6. Did you think Abe had more dreams than the other residents at Seven Oaks?

7. How did you feel about Abe's relationship with Ruby?

8. Do you think the residents at Seven Oaks were prejudiced?

9. How did you react to Ida's conflicting prejudices?

10. Do you think Abe was frustrated with Helen and felt like she just gave up without trying?

11. What do you think of Abe's relationship with Jake, his letter-writing friend?

12. Do you think Ida saved Abe in his stay at Seven Oaks?

13. What do you think Abe saw in Ida?

14. Do you think Abe was scared of losing his dependence? Do you have thoughts about this?

15. Do you think Ida was competitive at Seven Oaks?

16. Do you think Ida was disappointed with sex? Scared of sex?

17. Do you think running into Perry at Krogers was scary for Ida?

18. Do you think Ida was happy to rethink some of her childhood memories from this encounter?

19. Was Ida scared of Perry or her feelings?

20. Did Ida feel guilty of her mother's past prejudice towards Perry's family?

21. Do you think Perry's grandmother felt the same way about Ida's mother?

22. Do you think Ida idealized her relationship with Charlie after his death?

23. Do you think everyone at Seven Oaks was over-medicated? Have you seen this at assisted living facilities in real life?

24. Do you think Ida has always been depressed?

25. Do you think Abe can make her happy?

26. Do you think Sarah was jealous of Ida and Abe?

27. Do you think Abe can cure Ida of her pill addiction?

28. Do you think Abe and Ida will stay together for the rest of their lives?

29. Do you think Abe and Ida make a good couple?